8-WEEK COUPLES RELATIONSHIP THERAPY WORKBOOK

ACHIEVE LASTING RELATIONSHIP HEALTH, UNLOCK DEEPER EMOTIONAL CONNECTIONS, AND FOSTER SECURE ATTACHMENT THROUGH EFT (EMOTIONALLY FOCUSED THERAPY)

TAYLOR BLAKE

NORTH STAR PRESS

CONTENTS

INTRODUCTION

Have you ever found yourself lying awake at night, wondering if the person sleeping beside you is a stranger? The silence of the room punctuated only by the rhythm of their breath, a stark reminder of the distance that has crept between you. It's in these quiet moments that we confront the truth we often ignore during the daylight hours: the longing for a connection that once seemed unbreakable is now elusive. This book is your invitation to bridge that gap, to rediscover the intimacy and understanding that once defined your relationship. Let's embark on this journey together, exploring the paths leading back to each other's hearts.

Have you ever considered that the secret to deepening and enriching your connection with your partner might reside in carefully nurturing your emotional ties? With extensive experience addressing a wide range of issues in couples' therapy, I've discovered that Emotionally Focused Therapy (EFT) is an exceptionally effective method for those committed to achieving enduring relationship health and fostering secure attachments. This innovative approach, grounded in the profound principles of attachment theory, has transformed how we understand and cultivate love, offering a path to truly fulfilling relationships.

At the heart of EFT lies the conviction that our emotional attachments are central to our identity and well-being. Developed in the 1980s by Dr. Sue Johnson and Les Greenberg, EFT is a structured approach designed to address relationship distress and enhance emotional bonding. By focusing on attachment dynamics and employing experiential and systemic techniques, EFT has demonstrated remarkable success in helping couples create closer, more secure bonds.

One couple, teetering on the brink of separation, discovered that their frequent arguments were not the core issue but symptoms of a deeper emotional disconnect. As they learned to navigate their feelings and vulnerabilities with empathy and support, they rekindled a love they believed was lost. This story is just one of many that inspire my faith in EFT's potential to heal and strengthen relationships.

It is precisely these success stories, reflecting the depth and diversity of challenges couples face, that have fueled my dedication to extending the reach of EFT beyond the therapy room. As a seasoned life coach who has witnessed the transformative impact of EFT on numerous relationships, I felt compelled to distill my insights and strategies into an accessible 8-week program. This workbook, born from real-world applications and successes, is designed to bridge the gap for couples seeking profound change but not having immediate access to one-on-one therapy. By engaging with the exercises within these pages, couples everywhere can journey towards deeper connection and understanding, leveraging the principles of EFT to foster a lasting, loving partnership.

The "8-Week Couples Relationship Therapy Workbook" is your guided journey through the principles and practices of EFT. Structured to engage and empower, this workbook combines theoretical insights with practical exercises, real-life examples, and reflective opportunities to rejuvenate your partnership. Each week, we delve into key aspects of emotional bonding, communication, and conflict resolution, laying the groundwork for a more secure and fulfilling relationship.

How To Use This Workbook

Let's pause for a moment to explore the structure of this workbook. I've organized it into an 8-week thematic journey, a timeframe that has proven to be profoundly effective. Yet, the beauty of this program lies in its flexibility. Could you adapt it to 7, 10, or even 12 weeks? Absolutely. For instance, should you find yourselves with the luxury of time, perhaps during a vacation, and a keen desire to dive deeper at a more intense pace, advancing ahead of schedule is entirely possible. However, I recommend against compressing the experience into fewer than 6 weeks to ensure the most lasting and impactful results.

As you turn to the first week's chapter, you'll find a structured approach that unfolds the week's theme, complemented by a real-life case study and four or more collaborative exercises tailored for you and your partner. I designed this workbook to be a comprehensive guide, filled from cover to cover with valuable insights and tools. For exercises that require writing, you're welcome to use any method that suits you, from traditional pen and paper to digital tools. To enhance your experience, I've included a link to printable worksheets. Each worksheet is labeled with the corresponding week number and exercise name, ready for you to print, fill out, and use.

This workbook is designed with **40** carefully curated exercises, spread across eight weeks. Each week unfurls four to six opportunities designed to challenge and inspire. The quantity is meant to enrich, not overwhelm. After all, the heart of this workbook is your active participation and growth.

Worried about keeping track? Fear not! I have included a clear, easy-to-navigate Couples Connection Compass, showcased on the next page, which outlines the exercises week by week. Additionally, the same table, along with corresponding printable worksheets, is provided for your convenience.

Look for this heart symbol next to each exercise, both within the text and the Couples Connection Compass, to easily identify those exercises paired with a complementary worksheet.

Couples Connection Compass							
Timeline	**#**	**Exercise Name**		*Week 1*	*Week 2*	*Week 3*	*Week 4*
Week 1 - The Role of Attachment in Your Relationship	1	Attachment Style Mapping					
	2	Reflection Journal	♥				
	3	Attachment Style Role Play					
	4	Attachment Style Adjustment Plan	♥				
Week 2 - Deepening Emotional Intimacy	1	Daily Sharing Moments					
	2	Dreams and Fears	♥				
	3	36 Questions Intimacy Build					
	4	Emotional Intimacy Check Ins					
	5	Using Check-ins to Set Intimacy Goals					
	6	Celebrating Intimacy Growth					
Week 3 - Mastering Communication	1	Practicing "I" statements					
	2	Identifying Stress Signals	♥				
	3	Stress Communication Plan	♥				
	4	Building a Support System	♥				
Week 4 - The Fundamentals of Trust	1	Daily Trust Building					
	2	The Trust Jar					
	3	Long Term Trust Projects					
	4	Weekly Trust Check Ins	♥				
	5	Blindfolded Feeding Frenzy					

Couples Connection Compass						
Timeline	#	Exercise Name	Week 5	Week 6	Week 7	Week 8
Week 5 - Reigniting the Passion	1	Desire Mapping				
	2	Intimacy Ritual Creation				
	3	Guided Exploration				
	4	Bring It Up a Notch				
	5	Desire Discovery Dialogue				
Week 6 - Navigating Conflict with Compassion	1	Conflict Resolution Plan				
	2	Empathy in Action Role Play				
	3	Re-framing in Real Conflicts				
	4	The Future Letter				
	5	Time Capsule				
Week 7 - Individual Growth Within the Relationship	1	Digital Detox Date Night				
	2	Emotional Check In				
	3	Setting Digital Boundaries together				
	4	Digital Heart to Heart				
	5	Digital Space Respect				
	6	Dream Sharing Date Night				
Week 8 - Growing and Future Planning Together	1	Change Adaptation Plan				
	2	Role Playing Future Scenarios				
	3	Change Resilience Toolbox				
	4	Collaborative Vision Board				
	5	SMART Goals for Relationship				

Remember, there's no pressure to complete every exercise each week. With all its demands and surprises, life continues to unfold around us. The true beauty of this program lies in its flexibility. Simply tick off the exercises you've completed, keeping a gentle note of those you'd like to revisit—perhaps during a road trip or over dinner. These exercises are crafted to complement your lifestyle and enhance your connection, not to add to your burdens. Above all, take pride in the significant stride you've already made towards enriching your relationship by dedicating your time and engaging deeply with this material. This initial step is a commendable leap forward in nurturing a stronger, more fulfilling bond.

Embarking on this journey requires courage, openness, and a commitment to growth. Regardless of the stage of your relationship or the challenges you've faced, this workbook empowers you to transform your partnership. By the end of the 8-week program, you can expect not only improved communication skills and a deeper understanding of your emotional needs but also practical strategies for navigating disagreements and fostering a stronger bond.

Scan QR above to access complimentary worksheets

What sets this workbook apart is its evidence-based foundation, blending EFT principles with accessible exercises and real-life examples. Designed to be flexible, it accommodates your pace, acknowledging that every relationship is unique. Whether you seek to deepen your connection, resolve lingering conflicts, or simply understand your partner on a more profound level, this workbook offers a path to achieving those goals.

I invite you to commit to this 8-week journey with an open heart and mind empowered by a shared belief in your potential for change and growth as a couple. Active participation and reflection are key to unlocking the transformative power of this workbook. Let's begin the journey toward achieving the relationship you've always dreamed of.

WEEK 1 - THE ROLE OF ATTACHMENT IN YOUR RELATIONSHIP

In a world where connections are increasingly fleeting and superficial, the quest for enduring and meaningful relationships has never been more pressing. Emotional Focused Therapy (EFT) emerges as a beacon of hope for couples striving to deepen their bonds and navigate the complexities of modern love. This chapter introduces the transformative power of EFT, which is underpinned by solid scientific research and grounded in the principles of attachment theory. Through EFT, couples learn to communicate and connect on a level that fosters emotional security, mutual understanding, and genuine intimacy.

The Science Behind EFT: Why It Works

Research overwhelmingly supports the efficacy of EFT in enhancing relationship satisfaction. Couples who engage in EFT report significant improvements in emotional security and connection, laying a solid foundation for a lasting partnership.

EFT's success is rooted in attachment theory, which posits that the emotional bonds formed in early childhood influence our adult relationships. EFT leverages this insight to help couples understand their attachment styles and navigate their relationships' emotional landscapes more effectively.

At its core, EFT facilitates better emotional regulation, empowering individuals to manage their feelings in a way that promotes healthier interactions. This shift is crucial for breaking cycles of conflict and fostering a climate of mutual support.

EFT shifts the focus from surface-level disputes to underlying emotional needs, equipping couples with the tools to resolve conflicts through empathy and understanding rather than contention and withdrawal.

Understanding Attachment Styles and Their Impact on Relationships

Attachment styles are patterns of emotional bonding and interpersonal relationships originating from our earliest connections with caregivers. These styles significantly influence how individuals relate to their partners in adult relationships. Recognizing whether you or your partner tend towards a secure, anxious, or avoidant attachment style is the first step in navigating the complexities of your relationship dynamics. The three main attachment styles are secure, anxious, and avoidant.

Secure Attachment

Individuals with a secure attachment style are characterized by their comfort in both closeness and independence within relationships. They typically grew up in a supportive environment where caregivers were responsive to their needs, fostering a sense of security and self-worth. In adult relationships, securely attached individuals tend to be trusting, empathetic, and able to communicate openly and honestly. They are comfortable with intimacy and support their partners' independence. This balance allows for healthy, stable relationships where both partners feel valued and connected.

Anxious Attachment

Anxious attachment develops in individuals who experienced inconsistent caregiving in their early years. As adults, they often seek closeness and intimacy but may fear abandonment or rejection. Anxiously attached individuals can be overly preoccupied with their relationships, constantly seeking reassurance and validation from their partners. They may display clinginess, neediness, and heightened emotional responses to perceived threats to the relationship. This attachment style can lead to cycles of emotional highs and lows within relationships, with a tendency towards jealousy or controlling behaviors.

Avoidant Attachment

Avoidant attachment arises from a caregiving environment where emotional closeness and vulnerability were discouraged or not positively reinforced. Individuals with an avoidant attachment style value their independence to a high degree and often seem self-sufficient and reluctant to rely on others. They may struggle with intimacy in relationships, preferring to keep emotional distance from their partners. Avoidant individuals may come across as dismissive, aloof, or non-committal, often withdrawing in situations that require vulnerability or deep emotional connection. They might avoid deep emotional conversations and could be perceived as emotionally unavailable by their partners.

Fearful-Avoidant (Disorganized) Attachment

While the three primary attachment styles—secure, anxious, and avoidant—are often emphasized in the context of EFT, there is a fourth style, known as fearful-avoidant (also sometimes referred to as disorganized), which is acknowledged within the broader spectrum of attachment theory research. Individuals with a fearful-avoidant attachment style present a complex picture, as they do not fit neatly into the categories of the three more common styles. They harbor mixed feelings about close relationships, craving intimacy yet fearing potential harm,

3

which leads to a push-pull behavior that can perplex partners. Often, their ambivalence towards intimacy and trust can be traced back to a history of trauma or inconsistent caregiving in their early life.

These attachment styles manifest in relationships through behaviors, communication patterns, and emotional responses to relational dynamics. Understanding and addressing one's attachment style and recognizing the style of one's partner can significantly enhance relationship satisfaction and emotional connection by fostering empathy, improving communication, and facilitating healthier ways of relating to each other.

Impact on Relationship Dynamics

Differing attachment styles can lead to misunderstandings and conflict in relationships due to the distinct ways in which individuals perceive and respond to intimacy, emotional needs, and stress. These styles, formed in early childhood, fundamentally influence how we communicate, connect with others, and handle relationship challenges. Here's how the interplay of different attachment styles can lead to misunderstandings and conflicts:

- **Secure and Anxious Attachment:** A secure partner might not fully understand the constant need for reassurance and closeness exhibited by an anxious partner. The anxious partner may perceive the secure partner's comfort with independence and solitude as disinterest or neglect, leading to accusations, clinginess, or emotional turmoil. The secure partner, in turn, may feel overwhelmed or puzzled by the anxious partner's reactions, leading to frustration and a perceived lack of privacy or autonomy.
- **Secure and Avoidant Attachment:** A secure partner's willingness to engage in intimacy and emotional sharing may clash with an avoidant partner's preference for emotional distance and self-reliance. The avoidant partner might feel suffocated or pressured by attempts to increase closeness,

leading them to withdraw further. This withdrawal can be confusing and hurtful to the secure partner, who may struggle to understand why their attempts at fostering intimacy are being rebuffed.

- **Anxious and Avoidant Attachment:** This combination can create a cycle of push-and-pull dynamics, where the anxious partner's desire for closeness triggers the avoidant partner's need for space, leading to withdrawal. This withdrawal, in turn, heightens the anxious partner's fears of abandonment, causing them to cling tighter. The avoidant partner then feels more overwhelmed and further distances themselves, escalating the cycle of misunderstanding and conflict. This dynamic is often described as the "anxious-avoidant trap."

Mismatched Emotional Communication: Different attachment styles also mean different ways of communicating emotions. An anxious partner may express love through constant communication and seeking reassurance. In contrast, an avoidant partner might show love through acts of service or giving space, believing these actions respect independence and self-sufficiency. Such differences in expressing affection can lead to feelings of being unloved or uncared for simply because the expressions of love are not recognized or valued in the same way.

Conflict Resolution: How each style handles conflict can also lead to misunderstandings. Secure individuals may approach conflicts with a mindset geared towards resolution and compromise, anxious individuals may fear conflict will lead to abandonment and thus may either avoid addressing issues or become overly emotional, and avoidant individuals may shut down or withdraw from conflict, seeing it as a threat to their autonomy or a nuisance.

To navigate these challenges, partners must understand and respect their differing attachment needs, communicate openly about their emotional experiences, and work towards a balanced relationship dynamic that honors both partners' needs for closeness and independence. Recognizing and adapting to each other's attachment styles can foster empathy, reduce misunderstandings, and facilitate healthier conflict resolution strategies.

Path to Secure Attachment

Regardless of your starting point, EFT provides strategies to foster a move toward secure attachment, promoting a stable and fulfilling relationship. In our journey toward more profound connection and understanding within our relationships, recognizing and nurturing secure attachment is a fundamental goal. Secure attachment, characterized by feelings of safety, emotional openness, and mutual respect, provides a resilient foundation for lasting love and understanding.

The path to cultivating such secure bonds, regardless of one's initial attachment style—be it anxious, avoidant, or disorganized—begins with self-awareness and a willingness to grow. It's about creating a safe emotional space where both partners feel valued and heard.

- **Self-Reflection:** Start by exploring your own attachment style through introspection or with the help of a therapist. Understanding your emotional responses and relationship triggers can illuminate the path to change.
- **Communication:** Open, honest communication about needs, fears, and desires strengthens bonds—practice expressing your feelings in a non-threatening way, fostering an environment where vulnerability is met with empathy.
- **Responsive Action:** Adapt your behavior to respond more effectively to your partner's emotional needs. This might mean providing reassurance to an anxious partner or giving space to an avoidant one, always with the goal of moving toward more secure interactions.
- **Joint Activities:** Engage in activities that promote closeness and teamwork, reinforcing the bond and shared experiences. Whether it's a shared hobby or a couple's therapy session, these experiences can deepen your connection.

Case Study: Jordan and Casey

In my coaching practice, I worked with Jordan and Casey, a couple struggling with mismatched attachment styles. Jordan, exhibiting signs of anxious attachment, sought constant reassurance and closeness in their relationship. Casey, displaying avoidant tendencies, valued independence highly, often leading to feeling overwhelmed by Jordan's needs.

Through sessions focused on understanding and empathy, Jordan and Casey learned to navigate their differences constructively. Casey began to understand the importance of reassuring Jordan and being more present and engaged in the relationship. Meanwhile, Jordan worked on developing stronger self-confidence and independence, reducing the need for constant validation.

One pivotal strategy was their adoption of a weekly "relationship check-in." These check-ins provided a safe space for Jordan and Casey to express their feelings, discuss concerns, and celebrate successes. This practice improved communication and helped them understand and meet each other's needs more effectively.

The transformation in their relationship was profound. They moved from a cycle of anxiety and avoidance to a pattern of security and mutual support. Their journey is a testament to the power of understanding, communication, and commitment to growth, central to fostering secure attachment in any relationship.

By following a similar path and learning from the experiences of couples like Jordan and Casey, you can work towards creating a more secure, understanding, and loving connection with your partner.

Now that you have learned the basics of attachment styles let's start this week's exercises.

❦ ❦ ❦ ❦ ❦ ❦❦ ❦

Exercise 1: The Attachment Style Mapping

Objective: This exercise enhances self-awareness and mutual understanding of each partner's attachment style, laying the groundwork for deeper emotional connectivity.

Steps:

1. Each partner makes an initial guess about their and their partner's attachment style, writing these down for later comparison.
2. If you are not sure what your attachment style is or want to get your guess validated, you can take any of the reputable attachment style questionnaires available for free online, such as the one provided by Attachment Project https://quiz. attachmentproject.com/
3. After completing the test, compare your results with your initial guesses. Discuss any surprises or insights gained, focusing on how these attachment styles play out in your relationship dynamics.

Outcome: This exercise will foster open dialogue about your emotional needs and behaviors, paving the way for a deeper understanding and empathy within the relationship.

❦ ❦ ❦ ❦ ❦ ❦❦ ❦

Exercise 2: Reflection Journal

Objective: To deepen self-awareness about how each partner's attachment style influences their thoughts, feelings, and behaviors.

Let's Dive Deep Together: Take a personal journey through your journal this week.

See Worksheet

Each partner will keep a personal journal for one week, aiming for at least five entries. Included with this workbook, you'll find printable worksheets for each of you. Feel free to use it to gather your reflections.

Each day, reflect on moments that brought your attachment style into play. During a cozy cuddle or a challenging chat, jot down your feelings, thoughts, and reactions. Ask yourself:

• How did my heart feel in moments of connection or conflict today?

• What stories did my mind tell me when I felt secure or started to worry?

• How did I show up for my partner based on my feelings?

Sharing Is Caring: After this week of soul-searching, share your journey with your partner. This heart-to-heart is all about understanding how the dance of your attachment styles shapes your duo dynamics.

♥ ♥ ♥ ♥ ♥ ♥♥ ♥

Bridging the Attachment Gap

Navigating the complexities of attachment styles in relationships requires insight and intention. This section explores how various attachment styles can complement and clash within a relationship, offering strategies for couples to foster understanding, support, and, ultimately, a secure connection that benefits both partners.

The Complementarity and Conflict of Styles

Different attachment styles can both harmonize and create discord in a relationship. For instance, a partner with a secure attachment might offer stability and reassurance to an anxiously attached partner, creating a balance where each finds what they need in the other. However, challenges arise when, say, an avoidant partner's preference for emotional distance meets the anxious partner's need for closeness, leading to misunderstandings and frustration.

Recognizing and appreciating these dynamics are crucial. It's about seeing the unique perspective each attachment style brings to the table regarding intimacy and independence. The goal is not to change one another but to use these differences as a springboard for a stronger bond.

Strategies for Bridging the Gap

To effectively bridge the gap between differing attachment styles, consider these actionable steps:

- **Prioritize Open Communication:** Engage in transparent conversations about your needs, preferences, and concerns, focusing on expressing feelings without judgement
- **Invest in Understanding:** Take time to learn about each other's attachment styles. This knowledge can foster empathy and accommodate the needs specific to each style.
- **Find Shared Activities:** Look for interests and goals that satisfy both partners' needs for togetherness and autonomy and integrate these into your relationship routine.
- **Set Healthy Boundaries:** Develop clear boundaries that respect each partner's comfort levels, balancing closeness with necessary space.
- **Consider Professional Guidance:** Sometimes, a therapist can offer valuable perspectives and tools to navigate attachment styles more smoothly.

Creating a Secure Base

A relationship transforms into a secure base when trust, respect, and mutual support are at its core. This environment allows both partners to be vulnerable and authentic, knowing they are valued and understood. It's about assuring each other of a steady support system, where independence is celebrated, and emotional bonds are nurtured. Such a secure base is cultivated through consistent efforts to meet emotional needs, provide comfort, and encourage personal growth.

Exercise 3: Attachment Style Role-Play

Let's Step into Each Other's Shoes: This exercise is about deepening your empathy and getting a heartfelt glimpse into each other's attachment world.

How It Works:

- **Choose Your Scenes:** Pick moments from your recent past where you felt your attachment styles came into play.
- **Swap Roles:** Time to switch it up! Partner A takes on Partner B's attachment behavior and reactions, and vice versa. Dive deep into acting out what you think your partner was going through.
- **Reflect Together:** After the role-play, share what walking a mile in your partner's shoes was like. Was the portrayal spot on? How did it feel to see your behavior mirrored back?
- **Gain Insights:** Wrap up by sharing what you learned about lovingly supporting each other when those attachment-style moments arise again.

Exercise 4: The Attachment Style Adjustment Plan

Crafting Our Path Forward: Together, let's draw a map that leads us towards meeting each other's deepest needs, nurturing our bond every step of the way.

See Worksheet

Let's Get Started:

- **Spotlight on Needs:** Each of you jot down what you crave the most in terms of attachment—those emotional essentials that keep your heart full.
- **Strategize as a Team:** Now, brainstorm how you can bring those needs to life for each other. Think about specific, tangible ways to make each other feel loved and secure.
- **Set Our Goals:** Define clear, loving goals for this journey. How will you remind each other of this love and support daily?
- **Check-In Points:** Choose a future date to reflect on your achievements. Be open to tweaking your plan; after all, growth is about adapting and flourishing together.

Secure Attachment Building Activities

Now that you've delved into the world of secure attachment and pledged to bridge the gap between your attachment styles let's dive into a selection of heartwarming activities designed to draw you closer, knitting a tighter, more secure bond between you. With each step you take together, you're on the path to forging an even stronger connection, growing closer one shared moment at a time.

Activities to Explore Together:

- **Gratitude Moments:** Daily, let's tell each other one thing we genuinely appreciate. It's like giving your heart a warm hug.
- **Our Weekly Heart-to-Heart:** Set aside time every week for an open, honest chat about us—celebrating our wins and gently navigating our challenges.
- **Building trust Together:** Try activities that lean on trust, like partner yoga or cooking a meal together blindfolded. Feel the trust grow with each laugh and stumble.

- **Stroll Down Memory Lane:** Create a memory book or a shared digital photo album. Reliving these joy-filled moments can reignite that spark and strengthen our bond.
- **Dreaming Side by Side:** Regularly share and update each other on your dreams—both individual aspirations and those as a couple. It's like plotting the course of our shared adventure.
- **Let's Talk and Connect:** Engage in games that boost communication, revealing more profound layers of our hearts and minds in fun and playful ways.
- **Rituals of Affection:** Introduce small gestures of love into our daily routine, like a morning hug or an evening compliment, anchoring our day in love.

Embarking on these activities can infuse your relationship with joy, understanding, and a deep sense of security. Let's nurture our connection, making it stronger and more vibrant with each shared experience.

As we wrap up our exploration of attachment's role in relationships, let's harness this newfound understanding as we transition to the next phase of our journey. In the upcoming chapter, we'll delve into cultivating emotional intimacy, offering practical strategies to deepen connections and foster authentic closeness. So, instead of bidding farewell to attachment styles, let's carry their lessons forward, ready to embark on a path toward more prosperous, fulfilling relationships. Get ready to dive in and discover the transformative power of emotional intimacy.

WEEK 2 - DEEPENING EMOTIONAL INTIMACY

E mbarking on Week 2 of our journey, we focus on the heart of any strong relationship: deepening emotional intimacy. This week is about peeling back the layers, revealing the vulnerabilities and truths beneath the surface. It's about creating a safe space where fears and dreams can be shared without judgment, where every smile and tear is understood and valued. As we explore exercises and conversations designed to bring us closer, we'll learn that emotional intimacy isn't just about being physically close but about bridging the emotional distances between us. This week promises to strengthen the bonds of understanding and compassion, ensuring our connection grows deeper and more resilient with every shared experience. Let's dive into the depths of our hearts, uncovering the beauty of true emotional closeness.

The Layers of Emotional Intimacy

Welcome to the heart of our journey together. As your guide, I invite you to explore the profound essence of emotional intimacy, a critical element in cultivating a relationship that not only lasts but thrives. Emotional intimacy is about connecting on a level that goes beyond the everyday. It's about building a space where both partners feel seen, understood, and cherished. Let's delve into this together, uncovering the layers that lead to a genuinely fulfilling partnership.

Understanding Emotional Intimacy

At its core, emotional intimacy is about sharing the innermost parts of yourself with each other. It's about transparency and openness, where fears and dreams live side by side in shared conversations. This level of intimacy transforms your relationship into a sanctuary of mutual growth and support, making every challenge a bit easier to face, knowing you have a steadfast partner by your side. Acknowledging the importance of this connection is the first step toward cultivating a deeper bond.

Identifying Levels of Intimacy

Imagine emotional intimacy as a journey through a series of deeper and more meaningful landscapes. Initially, you start on the surface, sharing bits and pieces of your daily lives. As trust blossoms, you venture into more personal territories, discussing your values, aspirations, and, eventually, your vulnerabilities. Each level brings you closer, solidifying your connection. Understanding where you are on this journey can illuminate the path forward, guiding you to new depths of understanding and affection.

The Role of Vulnerability

Vulnerability is the key to deeper emotional intimacy. It's about daring to show your true self, including the parts you might want to hide. This courage to be vulnerable is not about weakness but about strength. It's a declaration that you trust your partner enough to see all of you. Creating a relationship where vulnerability is embraced and celebrated fosters a resilient and deeply affectionate connection.

Barriers to Intimacy

Even with the best intentions, barriers that cloud the path to emotional intimacy can arise. Fear of rejection might make you hesitant to share your true self, while past traumas can lead you to guard your heart closely. Recognizing these barriers is crucial, as is the commitment to work through them together. You can dismantle these walls through patience, empathy, and dedicated effort, paving the way for a deeper connection that celebrates openness and trust.

As we move forward, I'll share exercises and strategies designed to deepen your emotional bond. Remember, building emotional intimacy is a journey of continuous exploration and commitment to each other. It's about creating a shared space where both partners feel valued, understood, and deeply connected. Let's embark on this path together with open hearts and a shared vision of a more intimate and fulfilling relationship.

Sharing Inner Worlds: Activities for Deep Connection

As we journey deeper into your relationship's landscape, it's crucial to actively cultivate spaces that foster connection and understanding. It's in these spaces that you'll discover the power of shared vulnerability and the strength it brings. I want to introduce you to practices designed not just to share experiences but to deeply connect with each other's inner worlds. Let's explore these together, shall we?

❤ ❤ ❤ ❤ ❤ ❤❤ ❤

Exercise 1: Daily Sharing Moments

Imagine ending each day not with a summary of what happened but with a glimpse into each other's hearts. I encourage you to establish a practice of daily sharing moments. Each partner takes a turn to share something personal, perhaps a moment of joy, a challenge faced, or an insight gained. This practice isn't about problem-solving; it's about witnessing each other's day-to-day journey, offering a space where you're seen and heard.

❦ ❦ ❦ ❦ ❦ ❦❦ ❦

Exercise 2: Dreams and Fears

Objective: To forge a deeper bond by exchanging your most profound dreams and fears. Approach this exercise with an open heart, providing a safe space for your partner to be vulnerable.

See Worksheet

Instructions:

1. **Set the Scene:** Choose a tranquil moment free from distractions to engage in this exercise. The aim is to create an environment where both of you feel secure and undisturbed.
2. **Write It Down:** Individually, take some time to reflect and jot down your most cherished dream and your most significant fear. This step is personal and allows you to introspect before sharing.
3. **Share:** Begin taking turns to share what you've written down. As your partner speaks, listen with a heart full of empathy and understanding. This is a moment for listening deeply, not for offering solutions.
4. **Embrace Vulnerability:** Enter this exercise with an open and accepting heart. Offer your partner a sanctuary of understanding—a space where their dreams and fears are met with kindness and compassion.

Remember, this exercise is not just about speaking but about hearing and truly seeing your partner in their most vulnerable state. This shared vulnerability is a powerful step towards strengthening your emotional connection.

❧ ❧ ❧ ❧ ❧ ❧❧ ❧

Exercise 3: The "36 Questions" Intimacy Build

Based on psychological research, the "36 Questions for Increasing Closeness" exercise is a tool designed to accelerate intimacy. These questions progress from light-hearted to deeply revealing and are structured to foster mutual vulnerability and understanding. Incorporating this exercise into your relationship can be both fun and profoundly connecting.

Embark on a journey designed to deepen your connection and enhance emotional intimacy by exploring each other's inner worlds. This exercise, rooted in Dr. Arthur Aron's and his colleagues' pioneering work, invites you into a space of shared vulnerability and discovery.

Objective: Engage with your partner in a structured dialogue that promotes closeness and understanding. Foster an environment where vulnerability is seen as a strength, paving the way for deeper emotional connections.

How to Engage:

1. **Create a Space for Connection:** Set aside a special evening, free from distractions, and allow yourselves to be surprised by how much more there is to learn about each other. Choose a quiet, comfortable setting where you both can focus on each other without distractions.
2. **Have the Questions Handy:** Since the original "36 Questions for Increasing Closeness" developed by Dr. Arthur Aron form a scientifically backed sequence designed to accelerate intimacy between two individuals, I encourage you to use his meticulously crafted original set of questions, which could be found at https://ggia.berkeley.edu/practice/36_questions_for_in creasing_closeness. If you cannot open the URL, search for '36 Questions for Increasing Closeness' in your browser.

3. **Commit to the Process:** Follow the instructions closely, allowing both partners to share and listen actively. This exercise is as much about hearing and understanding your partner as it is about being heard.

Outcome: This exercise aims to fortify the bond between partners through shared vulnerability and empathy, deepen emotional intimacy and understanding, and uncover new, profound layers within each other's personal narratives and emotional landscapes.

♥ ♥ ♥ ♥ ♥ ♥♥ ♥

Remember, every couple's journey through vulnerability to intimacy is unique. Embrace this opportunity to explore the depth of your connection and the strength of your bond.

Emotional Intimacy Rituals

Rituals are the anchors of our relationships. They provide consistency and a sense of shared tradition. I suggest creating emotional intimacy rituals, such as weekly "heart-to-hearts." Dedicate this time to share feelings, experiences, and thoughts that have impacted you throughout the week. This ritual becomes a sacred space for emotional connection, a time to actively listen and empathize with each other's experiences.

These activities are not just tasks to check off; they are invitations to deepen your bond and profoundly understand each other. As you incorporate these practices into your relationship, remember that the journey of deepening intimacy is ongoing. It requires patience, dedication, and the courage to be vulnerable. Embrace this journey with open hearts, and let the deep connection you forge be the strength that sustains your relationship through all seasons.

Overcoming Intimacy Blocks

As you might anticipate, embarking on the journey to deep emotional intimacy comes with challenges. If it were easy, you would likely not invest in this workbook. Your commitment is the first step towards transformative growth in your relationship. Obstacles along the way are not just hurdles but opportunities for growth and deeper connection. In this section, we will explore how to identify, address, and navigate through intimacy blocks, fostering a stronger bond between you and your partner. Moreover, we'll look into the pivotal role of a supportive network in this journey. Let's embark on this transformative path together.

Recognizing Intimacy Blocks

The first step in overcoming any obstacle is recognizing it exists. Intimacy blocks can stem from many sources, including trust issues, communication barriers, past traumas, or fear of vulnerability. These blocks often manifest as hesitation to share feelings, avoidance of specific topics, or feeling disconnected even when together. Together, let's shine a light on these shadows, understanding that acknowledgment is the precursor to growth. Identifying these blocks is a joint effort that requires honesty, patience, and a willingness to be vulnerable.

Addressing Individual Blocks

Each person brings their unique history and experiences to a relationship, which can sometimes create personal barriers to intimacy. Addressing these requires a commitment to self-reflection and, when necessary, seeking external support through therapy. Engage in exercises designed to explore your inner self, such as journaling your thoughts and feelings, meditating on your emotional responses, and challenging your fears. This inward journey can reveal insights into how past experiences shape your current relationship dynamics, offering a roadmap to personal growth and improved emotional connection.

Navigating Intimacy Blocks as a Couple

While individual work is crucial, overcoming intimacy blocks is ultimately a team effort. Open communication is key. Create a safe space where both of you feel comfortable sharing your fears, desires, and vulnerabilities. Use active listening to truly hear and understand each other, responding with empathy and without judgment. Consider establishing a regular check-in routine where you can openly discuss your progress and any challenges you're facing. Remember, navigating these blocks together not only strengthens your bond but also deepens your mutual understanding and respect.

Building a Support Network

The journey toward overcoming intimacy blocks is not one to be walked alone. A supportive network of friends, family, or professionals can provide the external perspective and encouragement necessary to navigate challenging times. This network can include therapists specializing in couples counseling, support groups for relationship issues, or trusted loved ones who respect the sanctity of your partnership. Leaning on this support network can offer both comfort and practical advice, reinforcing the idea that overcoming these blocks is not just possible but a shared human experience

In summary, overcoming intimacy blocks is a multifaceted process that involves recognizing and addressing personal and relational challenges, navigating them as a united front, and drawing strength from a supportive community. This journey, while at times daunting, is an opportunity for profound personal and relational growth. Together, with commitment and compassion, you can break down these barriers, paving the way for a deeper, more fulfilling connection.

Emotional Intimacy Check-ins

I've witnessed firsthand the transformative power of deepening emotional intimacy between partners in my coaching practice. One particularly memorable example involves a couple, whom we'll call

Alex and Jordan, who came to me feeling disconnected despite years of marriage. They loved each other deeply but felt like they were drifting apart, unable to bridge the growing gap in their emotional connection.

Case Study - Alex and Jordan

Alex and Jordan had fallen into a routine that prioritized everything— work, children, social obligations—above their relationship. They communicated about logistics and daily responsibilities but rarely about their feelings, needs, or dreams. This lack of deep emotional sharing left them feeling lonely and misunderstood with their marriage.

I introduced them to weekly emotional intimacy check-ins during our sessions, a practice outlined in the next exercise. Hesitant at first, they committed to giving it a try. They chose Thursday evenings as their time after putting their children to bed, creating a cozy space in their living room with soft lighting and comfortable seating to make their conversations feel unique and distinct from their usual interactions.

The first few check-ins were challenging. Alex and Jordan struggled to move beyond surface-level conversations, often defaulting to discussing work or children. However, as they persisted, guided by the structured questions I provided, they gradually began to open up about more personal and vulnerable topics. They shared fears about losing each other, unmet needs within their relationship, and long-held dreams they had never voiced before.

A breakthrough came when Jordan shared a deep-seated fear of inade-quacy stemming from early childhood experiences, which had been affecting their ability to be fully present in the relationship. Alex, in turn, opened up about feeling overwhelmed by the pressure to be the perfect partner and parent, fearing failure. These confessions led to tears, understanding, and a level of emotional intimacy they hadn't experienced in years. Through their weekly check-ins, they learned to listen deeply, validate each other's feelings, and offer the support each needed.

As weeks turned into months, Alex and Jordan transformed their relationship. They set and achieved intimacy goals, such as dedicating time to pursue shared hobbies and scheduling recurring date nights to focus on each other without distractions. They celebrated their progress, acknowledging how these check-ins had become a cherished part of their week, eagerly anticipated by both.

Their story is a powerful testament to the effectiveness of intentional, structured emotional sharing in fostering a deep, fulfilling connection between partners. Alex and Jordan's journey from feeling disconnected to rediscovering their emotional bond exemplifies the profound impact of prioritizing emotional intimacy on a relationship. It's a vivid reminder that, with commitment and the right tools, couples can navigate the challenges of intimacy together, strengthening their bond and enhancing their love in ways they never thought possible.

♥ ♥ ♥ ♥ ♥ ♥♥ ♥

Exercise 4: Your First Emotional Check-In

Objective: Establish a ritual to build a deeper connection and enhance emotional intimacy between partners through the establishment of a weekly check-in ritual. This practice aims to create a sacred space for both partners to openly share their feelings, needs, and experiences, fostering a stronger, more understanding bond.

Creating Our Sacred Space Together:

This week, embark on a meaningful journey to solidify your commitment to each other's emotional well-being by establishing a weekly check-in ritual. These moments are your sanctuary for reflection, connection, and growth.

Steps:

1. **Selecting Our Time and Place:** Together, choose a day and time each week that you can dedicate to one another without

distractions. Treat this as a paramount appointment, honoring it with the same importance as any other non-negotiable engagement. Find a spot where you both feel at ease expressing yourselves freely, ensuring privacy and comfort.

2. **Setting the Scene:** Transform your chosen space into a haven for heartfelt dialogue. This might mean silencing your phones, dimming the lights, or arranging a cozy seating area that welcomes openness and vulnerability. The goal is to create an environment that feels secure and inviting, conducive to genuine exchange.

3. **Guided Prompts for Our Check-Ins:** As you settle into your newly established ritual, use the guided prompts below to navigate your discussions. These questions are designed to peel back the layers of your daily experiences, allowing you to explore the emotional depths of your relationship.

4. **Reflect and Respond:** Take turns sharing your thoughts and feelings. Listen actively, without planning your response, while your partner speaks. This exercise is about understanding each other on a deeper level, not about solving problems immediately.

Guided Prompts for Our Check-Ins:

Begin with any of the suggested prompts below, or choose to craft your own. Over time, as you integrate this check-in practice into your routine, you'll find that the need for written cues may diminish. In my experience, couples dedicated to growth often thrive on natural, organic conversations. Nevertheless, this collection serves as a solid starting point to catalyze your discussions:

Reflecting on Our Week:

- What were the highlights of your week, and why do they stand out to you?
- Were there moments this week when you felt particularly

close to or distant from me? What happened, and how did it make you feel?

Exploring Emotional Landscapes:

- Describe a moment from this week when you experienced a strong emotion, whether it was joy, sadness, frustration, or something else. What sparked this feeling?
- How did this emotion influence your behavior towards me and others?

Understanding Each Other's Needs:

- Is there something you need more of from me or our relationship right now?
- Are there ways we can support each other better in the coming week?

Celebrating Our Strengths:

- What is one thing I did this week that made you feel loved or supported?
- Share a quality or action of yours that you feel positively impacted our relationship this week.

Navigating Challenges Together:

- If we encountered any conflicts or challenges this week, how do we feel about how we handled them?
- What can we learn from how we navigated these situations, and how might we approach things differently in the future?

Expressing Gratitude and Affirmations:

- Share something you are particularly grateful for in our current relationship.
- Offer an affirmation or positive wish for your partner and your relationship moving forward.

Closing Our Check-In:

- **Reflecting on Our Conversation**: How did today's check-in make you feel? Do you feel closer or have new insights into our relationship?
- **Affirming Our Commitment:** Let's affirm our commitment to these weekly check-ins and to continuously fostering our emotional intimacy.

These prompts are designed to guide you through a deep and meaningful exploration of your emotional worlds, helping both partners feel seen, heard, and valued in the relationship. Remember, the goal is not to solve all issues in one discussion but to cultivate an ongoing practice of openness and understanding.

🖤 🖤 🖤 🖤 🖤 🖤🖤 🖤

Exercise 5: Using Check-Ins to Set Intimacy Goals

In our final week together, we'll focus on goal setting, where we'll master the art of establishing SMART goals specifically tailored to enrich your relationship. This structured approach will guide us in setting clear, achievable objectives, ensuring that your future together is envisioned and planned with intention and clarity. However, before we reach that point, I encourage you to begin weaving discussions about your goals into your regular Check-Ins. This practice will help make goal-setting a natural part of your relationship's rhythm, laying the groundwork for more formal planning in our concluding sessions.

Identify Growth Areas: Discuss aspects of your emotional intimacy you both wish to enhance. Be specific about what you desire more of, such as understanding, patience, or shared vulnerabilities.

Setting Intentions for Growth:

- Looking ahead, what is one thing each of us can focus on to strengthen our bond in the coming week?
- Are there specific areas in our relationship where we could improve or deepen our connection?

Set Actionable Goals: For each identified area, outline practical steps you can take. Assign achievable tasks for both partners and set a timeline to revisit these goals.

Exercise 6: Celebrating Intimacy Growth

- **Acknowledge Achievements:** At the start or end of each check-in, take time to celebrate the progress you've made towards your intimacy goals. This could be recognizing efforts to be more open, appreciating the support provided during a challenging time, or simply maintaining the ritual of your weekly check-ins.
- **Reinforce Positive Changes:** Use positive reinforcement to encourage continued growth. Highlight specific actions or words that significantly impacted your emotional connection.

By dedicating time each week to focus on your relationship's emotional well-being through these exercises, you create a dynamic space for growth, understanding, and deeper connection. These check-ins are about navigating challenges and celebrating your journey together, reinforcing the bond that deepens with every shared experience.

As we conclude the second week, focused on deepening emotional intimacy, you and your partner have engaged in meaningful exercises that pave the way toward a richer, more connected relationship. You both have dedicated this past week to uncovering and appreciating the emotional landscapes that shape your bond, acknowledging vulnerabilities, and reinforcing the ties that bind you with trust, empathy, and unconditional love. With these foundational stones of a profound emotional connection now in place, we look ahead to mastering the art of communication in the upcoming week. The skills and insights gained through these explorations are crucial for building a lasting, healthy relationship and fostering a secure attachment. Let's move forward with the understanding and breakthroughs from this week, ready to enhance our communication and deepen our connection even further.

WEEK 3 - MASTERING COMMUNICATION

Mastering communication is not merely about conveying information; it's about connecting hearts, healing wounds, and building a bridge of understanding and respect between partners. In this chapter, we'll explore the pivotal aspects of communication that can significantly enhance your relationship. Let's embark on this journey together, transforming how we express ourselves and perceive our partners.

Active Listening for Conflict Resolution

Active listening is more than just hearing words; it's a transformative skill that turns conflicts into opportunities for growth and deeper understanding. By employing specific techniques such as maintaining eye contact, reflecting on what has been said for clarity, and asking open-ended questions, partners can effectively de-escalate conflicts and foster a sense of empathy and connection. Practicing active listening through role-play scenarios allows couples to refine these skills in a safe environment, making them more adept at handling real-life disputes. Moreover, recognizing and avoiding common missteps, such as interrupting or preparing a rebuttal while the other person is speaking, is crucial. By focusing on truly understanding each other's perspectives, active listening becomes a powerful tool for strengthening relationships and turning potential conflicts into pathways for intimacy and mutual respect.

Expressing Yourself Assertively

Assertiveness allows you to articulate your needs and feelings with precision, ensuring that communication within your relationship remains balanced and respectful. It's essential to recognize that assertiveness isn't about bulldozing over someone's feelings or being combative; it's about articulating your views and boundaries in a confident yet considerate way.

Think of assertiveness as establishing a common ground in a vast landscape of conversation, where both partners can stand firmly, express themselves openly, and still hold hands. This begins with a deep dive into self-awareness: identifying your desires, emotions, and limits. Then, moving forward with the practice of voicing these truths in a manner that's straightforward yet compassionate, using "I" statements that focus on your experiences without placing fault.

Imagine you're on the verge of a disagreement, and instead of withdrawing into silence or escalating the conflict, you choose to share your feelings calmly and listen to your partner with an open heart. Or consider a moment when you need to set a boundary, doing so with firmness and empathy, ensuring both of you feel heard and respected.

Adopting assertiveness during these moments of interaction becomes more than a mere communication technique; it evolves into a foundation for a relationship where transparency and mutual respect are paramount. As we navigate this process together, I'm here to support you every step of the way, encouraging you to let your true self be seen and heard, fostering a dynamic of genuine understanding and respect.

The Power of "I" Statements

In the landscape of communication, "I" statements stand as a beacon, guiding conversations away from the rocky shores of blame and towards the calm waters of understanding. They're a potent tool for expressing yourself clearly and respectfully while remaining centered on your feelings and experiences.

Structure of an Effective "I" Statement: At its core, an "I" statement is a personal declaration that expresses your feelings, connects them to a specific behavior, and explains the effect of that behavior on you. The formula is straightforward yet powerful:

I feel [emotion] **when** [specific behavior] **because** [explanation].

This structure is pivotal in turning a potentially accusatory statement into one that invites empathy and understanding, paving the way for constructive dialogue.

♥♥ ♥♥ ♥♥ ♥♥ ♥♥ ♥♥♥♥ ♥♥

Exercise 1: Practice Crafting "I" Statements.

Objective: Transform thoughts and feelings into "I" statements to enhance emotional clarity and foster constructive communication.

They say there's no 'I' in 'teamwork,' but throw in some 'I' statements, and suddenly it's 'Teamwork: Now featuring I!' – a special edition where everyone feels heard! This exercise is a comprehensive journey into the heart of effective communication, focusing on the transformative power of "I" statements. Over this week, you'll engage in a three-part practice designed to deepen your understanding and application of "I" statements in various contexts of your relationship. Although this reflective practice can be carried out individually, practicing it as a shared activity will provide added insight.Steps:

1. **Emotion Reflection:** Throughout the week, keep a daily log of moments that trigger strong emotions in you. For each event,

describe your feelings using the "I feel [emotion] when [specific behavior] because [reason]" format. This exercise aims to cultivate self-awareness around your emotional responses and the situations that evoke them.

2. **From "You" to "I":** Identify instances where you might typically use "You make me feel..." statements. Convert these sentences into "I" statements that clearly express your feelings without laying blame. This practice encourages a shift from a potentially accusatory stance to one of personal responsibility for your emotions.

3. **Role-Play for Empathy:** Set aside a moment for a role-play exercise between the two of you. Share stories that push your emotional buttons, whether pulled from your day or entirely made up. Make sure to frame your experiences with 'I' statements, shining a light on your inner landscape. This part of the exercise is designed to enhance your ability to communicate effectively, even in the heat of the moment, and to practice active listening when it's your partner's turn to share.

4. **Reflection:** Review your daily logs at the end of the week and reflect on the following questions: *How has my understanding of "I" statements deepened through this practice? In what ways did shifting from "You" to "I" change the dynamics of my conversations? How did the role-play exercise impact my ability to listen and respond empathetically?*

5. **Sharing:** Share your insights and experiences from the week with each other. Discuss how "I" statements can enhance your communication and deepen your connection. This shared reflection is an opportunity to explore how both partners can support each other in continuing to use "I" statements as a tool for healthy, constructive communication in your relationship.

❦ ❦ ❦ ❦ ❦ ❦❦ ❦

Impact of "I" Statements on the Listener: When we shift from *"You did this"* to *"I feel this,"* we move away from casting blame to sharing our perspective. "I" statements lower the defensive walls that accusatory language often builds, making it more likely for your partner to hear you, empathize, and engage in a meaningful conversation. This approach doesn't just reduce defensiveness; it opens a gateway to deeper emotional connections by fostering an environment where both parties feel safe to express their true selves.

In essence, "I" statements are more than just a communication strategy; they're a pathway to authenticity and empathy in your relationships. By focusing on your feelings and experiences, you invite a dialogue that respects both your perspective and your partner's, nurturing a bond built on mutual understanding and care.

Navigating Difficult Conversations

Difficult conversations are a natural part of life's ebb and flow of any relationship. While they may seem daunting, these conversations offer rich soil for growth and understanding when approached with care and the right strategies.

Preparing for Difficult Conversations: Before diving into deep waters, anchoring yourself can make all the difference. Here's how:

- Reflect on your goals for the conversation. What do you hope to achieve or clarify?
- Consider your partner's perspective and potential feelings to foster empathy from the start.
- Calm your nerves and clear your mind through deep breathing or a moment of quiet, setting a foundation of tranquility for the discussion ahead.

Guidelines for Conducting Difficult Conversations: With preparation complete, these steps can help guide your conversation towards constructive shores:

1. Choose a peaceful setting, free from distractions, where both of you feel comfortable and safe.
2. Begin with affirming the value of your relationship and your intention to understand and resolve the issue at hand.
3. Use "I" statements to express your feelings and perspectives without placing blame, keeping the dialogue centered on understanding each other.
4. Listen actively, showing your partner that their feelings and viewpoints are valid and important to you.
5. Navigate the conversation with patience and openness, ready to find common ground or agree to revisit the discussion later if emotions run high.

Follow-up After Difficult Conversations: The journey doesn't end when the conversation does. Follow-up is key to reinforcing the bridges built through dialogue.

- Revisit the conversation after some time has passed to ensure both partners feel heard and understood.
- Acknowledge any progress made towards the goals set before the conversation, appreciating the effort from both sides.
- Discuss and agree on actionable steps moving forward, ensuring that the conversation translates into positive changes or solutions.

By embracing these practices, difficult conversations can transform from daunting challenges into opportunities for strengthening the bonds of your relationship, ensuring that both partners feel valued, understood, and respected.

Case Study - Chris and Jordan

In my practice, I worked with a couple, let's call them Chris and Jordan. After four years together, they were at a crossroads due to recurring conflicts over financial planning and future aspirations. Despite their commitment, discussions about money often spiraled into arguments, leaving both feeling unheard and disconnected. Seeking to break this cycle, they approached me for guidance on improving their communication.

We embarked on a strategy focusing on self-reflection, allowing each partner to identify their financial fears and goals. This groundwork paved the way for a crucial conversation in a calm and chosen setting to encourage openness and attentiveness. Guided by the principle of starting with affirmations of mutual respect and shared dreams, Chris and Jordan were coached to use "I" statements, enabling them to express their individual perspectives without laying blame.

This technique fostered a newfound understanding between them. Chris voiced concerns about long-term security, while Jordan highlighted the importance of enjoying life's journey. This balanced exchange led to a deeper empathy and recognition of common goals.

Following this turning point, they committed to regular check-ins to monitor their financial plans and continue refining their communication. In addition to helping them manage their fiances, these meetings significantly strengthened their relationship, showcasing the power of thoughtful dialogue and mutual support in overcoming challenges.

The Role of Humor in Communication

In the intricate web of human connection, humor gleams as a thread that can both connect and complicate. Within the sanctuary of a partnership, when wielded with care and sensitivity, humor emerges as a powerful tool to bond, lighten burdens, and bridge gaps in understanding.

Understanding the Boundaries of Humor: The art of humor in communication lies in its precision—dance on the edge of light-heartedness and sensitivity. Couples must recognize and understand that what brings joy and exhilaration to one partner might, without intention, cause emotional hurt or discomfort to the other. The key is to navigate this landscape deeply, understanding each other's emotional boundaries, ensuring that humor acts as a bridge rather than a barrier.

In the case of Brian and Ana from my practice, Brian, being a few years younger than Ana, occasionally made light-hearted jokes about their age difference. Initially, these comments were met with laughter and seen as nothing more than playful teasing. Yet, as these remarks persisted, they started to grate on Ana. It wasn't that she felt insecure about her age; rather, she began to question why Brian felt the need to repeatedly highlight this difference. This situation serves as a reminder of how humor, even when not intended to harm, can become annoying and lead to misunderstandings if overused or focused on a single topic.

Examples of Humor Enhancing Communication: Consider the moments when a playful quip defuses an escalating argument or when shared laughter in the face of adversity tightens your bond. Such instances underscore humor's potential to transform a tense atmosphere into one of connection and shared resilience. Humor, when used with intention and care, can be a lifeline—pulling partners back to the surface when the waters of communication grow too heavy.

Developing a Shared Sense of Humor: Cultivating a shared sense of humor is akin to creating your own private language—one that deepens intimacy and fosters a unique complicity between partners. This can be nurtured through shared experiences, be it watching comedies that tickle both your funny bones, reminiscing over inside jokes, or playfully teasing within the bounds of affection and respect. Over time, this shared humor becomes a cornerstone of your relationship, a secret weapon that empowers you to face life's challenges with a smile.

Humor, in its essence, is a gift—an elixir that can heal, reveal, and unite. In the realm of relationships, it offers a light touch that can ease difficult conversations, illuminate common ground, and weave joy into the fabric of daily life. As couples journey together, learning to laugh with each other (and sometimes, at themselves) becomes not just a method of communication, but a celebration of their shared life and love.

Recognizing and Stopping Unhealthy Communication Patterns

Navigating the currents of communication with care and awareness is essential for the health and vitality of your partnership. Just as a garden thrives with attention and nurturing, so too does the connection between partners flourish when tended with positive communication habits. Identifying and transforming negative communication patterns into constructive dialogues is a cornerstone of this nurturing process.

Common Unhealthy Communication Patterns:

- **Criticism:** Attacking your partner's character or personality instead of addressing specific behaviors or actions.
- **Defensiveness:** Responding to feedback with excuses or counter-complaints instead of openness to your partner's perspective.
- **Contempt:** Communicating with disrespect, sarcasm, or mockery, undermining the dignity of your partner.
- **Stonewalling:** Withdrawing from the conversation or relationship to avoid conflict, leaving issues unresolved.

Strategies for Breaking Patterns:

- **Mindful Recognition:** The first step is acknowledging the existence of these patterns within your communication dynamics. This awareness creates a platform for change.
- **Understanding Triggers:** Together, explore what triggers these negative patterns. Is it stress, specific topics, or particular behaviors? Understanding these triggers allows you to prepare and respond differently.
- **Pause and Reflect:** Before responding habitually, take a moment to pause. This brief interlude can help you choose a response that promotes a healthier communication pattern.
- **Use "I" Statements:** Shift from blame to expressing your

feelings and needs. This approach encourages openness and understanding, reducing the likelihood of defensiveness.

Creating New, Healthy Communication Habits:

- **Regular Check-Ins:** Establish a routine for checking in with each other about your feelings, experiences, and needs. This consistent communication fosters a culture of openness and attentiveness.
- **Active Listening:** Practice truly listening to understand, not to reply. This means giving your full attention, reflecting on what you've heard, and asking questions to deepen understanding.
- **Express Appreciation:** Make it a habit to express appreciation and gratitude for each other. Recognizing and vocalizing the positive aspects of your partner and your relationship strengthens your bond.
- **Set Goals Together:** Collaboratively set goals for your communication and relationship. Having shared objectives can motivate both partners to engage in healthier communication practices.

Transforming unhealthy communication patterns into constructive habits is a journey that requires patience, commitment, and mutual support. By embracing these strategies, couples can cultivate a relationship environment where understanding and respect bloom, enabling both partners to grow together in love and harmony.

The Importance of Silence and Space

In a relationship, moments of silence and spaces of solitude are not merely absences of sound or presence; they are profound acts of communication in their own right. Embracing silence and space within a partnership can lead to a deeper connection, fostering an environment where both individuals feel understood, respected, and valued.

The Value of Silence in Listening: Silence can be a sanctuary for reflection and growth when integrated into our daily interactions. It allows both partners to process their thoughts and emotions, creating a deeper understanding of each other's perspectives. In these quiet moments, we allow ourselves to absorb the essence of our partner's words, transcending the superficial layers to reach the heart of their message. Silence, therefore, becomes a bridge to empathy, a pause that invites us to inhabit our partner's world with greater compassion and insight.

Communicating the Need for Space: Articulating the need for personal space is a delicate dance, requiring honesty tempered with sensitivity.

Articulating a desire for personal space is a nuanced affair that, when approached with care, nurtures the relationship. It begins with recognizing that this need is not a rejection but a vital aspect of individual well-being. When expressing your need for space, clarify that it's an opportunity for self-reflection and rejuvenation, not a retreat from the relationship. Use "I" statements to convey your feelings and reassure your partner of your commitment, emphasizing that this space is about nurturing your ability to be a more present and engaged partner.

Case Study - Emily and Alex

In my practice, I encountered Emily and Alex, a couple navigating the delicate balance between their differing morning routines. Emily, whose mornings were fueled by vibrant energy, looked forward to starting her day by sharing thoughts and engaging deeply with Alex. In contrast, Alex valued a serene start, using his mornings for meditation and to introspectively gather his thoughts before facing the day ahead.

The turning point for Emily and Alex came through a process of open communication, a testament to their commitment to understanding each other's needs. Alex introduced "I" statements into their dialogues and expressed his feelings. This heartfelt admission illuminated for

Emily the importance of this solitude for Alex's well-being and their relationship's health.

Acknowledging Alex's needs, Emily embraced a period of calm coexistence in their mornings, finding joy in the quiet as a form of connection. In return, Alex recognized Emily's need for morning interaction and began to seek out moments after his period of reflection where he could engage fully and enthusiastically with her, sharing in the vibrant energy she brought to the start of their day.

This adjustment in their morning routine became a beautiful dance of give-and-take, a daily practice of honoring each other's needs while nurturing their bond. Emily and Alex's journey underscores the power of effective communication and the role of understanding and compromise in strengthening a relationship. Their story reminds us that even in silence, love speaks volumes, and we find a closer connection in giving space to each other.

Respecting Your Partner's Need for Space: Honoring your partner's request for solitude is a testament to the strength and maturity of your relationship. It acknowledges that personal growth and fulfillment are integral to the health of the partnership. Respecting this space demonstrates trust and understanding, foundational to love's endurance. By supporting each other's need for solitude, you cultivate a relationship where individuality and togetherness coexist in harmony, each enriching the other.

Silence and space, far from being signs of distance or disconnection, are essential components of a healthy relationship. They offer moments of introspection and renewal, enabling partners to return to each other with renewed spirit and deeper appreciation. In learning to cherish these quiet interludes and respites of solitude, couples discover new depths of connection and communication, ensuring their relationship remains vibrant and resilient through the changing seasons of life.

Communicating During Stressful Times

In the ebb and flow of life, stress is an inevitable undercurrent that can muddy the waters of communication between partners. Recognizing and navigating these turbulent times with clarity and compassion can fortify a relationship, transforming potential rifts into strengthened bonds.

Identifying Stress-Induced Communication Barriers: Stress can stealthily infiltrate communication, erecting barriers that distort messages and intentions. Signs of stress impacting communication include shortened tempers, an inability to listen effectively, and a tendency towards negative interpretations. Recognizing these signs is the first step in addressing the underlying stress, allowing couples to approach discussions with greater understanding and patience.

Adjusting Communication in Response to Stress: When stress looms large, altering your communication strategy can make a world of difference. Here are a few strategies:

- **Prioritize Listening:** Make a conscious effort to listen more intently, giving your partner your full attention, affirming that you are there for them.
- **Speak Calmly and Clearly:** Use a calm tone to convey your thoughts and feelings, focusing on using "I" statements to express how you're affected by the situation.
- **Take Timeouts:** If emotions escalate, agree to take a brief break from the discussion, allowing both partners to cool down and collect their thoughts before continuing.

Support Systems and Stress Relief: Beyond adjusting communication techniques, leaning on external support systems and engaging in stress relief activities can significantly improve how stress is managed within a relationship. Encourage each other to pursue individual hobbies or relaxation techniques such as exercise, meditation, or spending time in nature. Additionally, seeking the support of friends, family, or a professional can provide new perspectives and coping strategies.

Moreover, developing a joint stress relief routine can be beneficial. Whether it's a weekly date night, a shared hobby, or simply taking a walk together, find activities that help both partners unwind and reconnect. These moments of togetherness become sanctuaries from the stress of the outside world, reinforcing the bond and improving the quality of communication.

Communicating during stressful times demands a heightened level of awareness, empathy, and flexibility. By recognizing the impact of stress on communication, consciously adjusting your communication approach, and utilizing support systems for stress relief, couples can navigate these challenging periods with grace, emerging stronger and more connected on the other side

Stress can cast a long shadow over communication, obscuring the love and respect partners typically share. The next three exercises covered in this chapter are designed to help you recognize when stress is impacting your interactions and adopt strategies that preserve the integrity of communication during these challenging times. Through reflection, practice, and support, partners can strengthen their ability to navigate stressful periods together.

Exercise 2: Identifying Stress Signals

Objective: To enhance understanding and empathy between partners during periods of stress, maintaining clarity and compassion in communication.

See Worksheet

Steps:

1. **Individual Reflection:** Each partner dedicates time to individually explore their own stress indicators—those physical, emotional, and behavioral signs that signal the onset of stress. This could manifest in various ways, such as becoming more withdrawn, exhibiting signs of irritability, or experiencing sleep disruption. This process of reflection can be seamlessly integrated into your daily routine; for instance, contemplate these stress signals during your morning commute and jot down your observations on your phone. This ensures you capture these insights accurately for later discussion.

2. **Shared Insights:** Come together and share your findings. Discuss how these stress signals might affect your communication and behavior towards each other. During this exchange, explore whether your partner has observed any additional stress signals that you may not have been consciously aware of in yourself. Reflect together on the reasons for these differences in perception, considering the possibility that external viewpoints can reveal aspects of ourselves we may overlook.

Outcome: Upon completing the Identifying Stress Signals exercise, you will have a deeper understanding of each other's stress-related behaviors and responses. This newfound awareness will enable you to navigate stressful situations with increased empathy and support, enhancing the care you provide for one another in those crucial moments.

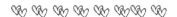

Exercise 3: The Stress Communication Plan

"By failing to prepare, you are preparing to fail." – Benjamin Franklin. Embracing this wisdom, let's construct a Stress Communication Plan, a foundational strategy designed to fortify your relationship against the inevitable

pressures of life. This plan is not just about bracing for tough times; it's about actively shaping an environment where understanding and connection can thrive, even amidst stress.

- **Creating a Safe Word/Signal:** Select a word or signal that both of you can use when the stress of the moment makes effective communication challenging. This will act as your relationship's pause button, a discreet yet powerful way to signal the need for a break or a strategic shift in the conversation. Choose something unique yet unobtrusive, allowing you to employ it in public spaces if necessary, thereby offering a means to gently recalibrate your interaction on the spot.
- **Developing Stress-Responsive Communication Strategies:** Together, outline ways to adjust your communication during times of stress. This could involve strategies like pausing to take a series of deep breaths before responding, deliberately using "I" statements to share your feelings without assigning blame or making a mutual decision to postpone difficult discussions until a moment of calm or after engaging in stress-relieving activities. This proactive approach to communication under stress ensures that both partners feel heard, respected, and valued, even in the most challenging times.
- Over the following week, put your Stress Communication Plan into action. Be mindful of each other's stress signals and utilize your agreed-upon strategies and support systems to navigate moments of heightened tension.

- At the end of the week, reflect on the experience. Discuss what worked well, any challenges you faced, and adjustments you can make to improve how you communicate under stress in the future.

Outcome: Upon completing the Stress Communication Plan exercise, you will have established a personalized framework designed to enhance your communication during stressful moments, ensuring that both partners feel heard, understood, and supported, thereby strengthening your emotional connection and resilience as a team.

❧ ❧ ❧ ❧ ❧ ❧❧ ❧

Exercise 4: Building a Support System

Objective: Collaboratively identify and integrate various forms of support into your lives, enhancing your resilience to stress both individually and as a couple. By recognizing and actively engaging with sources of support, you cultivate a stronger, more supportive partnership capable of navigating challenges with greater ease and understanding.

See Worksheet

- **Identifying Sources of Support:** Make a list of activities, practices, or people that serve as stress relief and support for each of you individually and as a couple. This could include exercise, hobbies, spending time with loved ones, or seeking professional support.
- **Incorporating Support into Routine:** Commit to integrating these support systems into your daily or weekly routines, ensuring that both partners have access to stress relief resources that can help maintain healthy communication.
- **Practice and Reflection:** This exercise is not a one-time solution but a starting point for developing deeper understanding and empathy for each other's experiences of

stress. Regularly revisiting and refining your Stress Communication Plan will strengthen your partnership and make you more resilient in life's inevitable stresses.

Outcome: Upon completing this exercise, you'll have a dynamic map of personal and mutual support havens seamlessly integrated into your routines. This isn't just about having a list; it's about creating a lifestyle that embeds resilience and joy into the very heart of your relationship. Regularly revisiting this map, adapting and expanding it, will ensure that no matter what life throws at you, you'll navigate it with strength, understanding, and a deep-seated assurance that you're in this together, supported and stronger than ever.

❦ ❦ ❦ ❦ ❦ ❦❦ ❦

As we wrap up Week 3 on Mastering Communication, it's clear that the heart of a thriving relationship is not just in speaking, but in being truly heard and understood. This week has equipped you with essential tools and strategies to enhance how you express yourselves and listen to one another, ensuring that every word and every silence builds a bridge to deeper connection. As we pivot to Week 4, focusing on the Fundamentals of Trust, remember that the strong communication foundation you've built is the bedrock upon which trust is established and nurtured. In the coming week, we'll explore how to leverage this foundation to foster an environment of trust and security, where both partners feel valued, understood, and unequivocally supported—no matter what challenges you come against together.

WEEK 4 - THE FUNDAMENTALS OF TRUST

A t the heart of every enduring relationship lies trust, a complex yet crucial element that nurtures the relationship's growth and depth of connection. Through my personal experiences and professional observations, I've seen trust as the adhesive that binds relationships and as the foundational bedrock enabling love to grow and mature. In this chapter, we will explore the multifaceted nature of trust, dissecting its key components and the subtle dynamics that either strengthen or weaken its presence. Through a detailed examination of trust's role in romantic partnerships, we will equip you with the insights and strategies necessary to cultivate a bond characterized by confidence, transparency, and deep mutual respect.

Understanding the Elements of Trust

Trust in a romantic relationship comprises numerous essential elements, each contributing to its strength and resilience. It forms the cornerstone upon which a relationship's stability rests, is complex in composition, and is crucial for deep, lasting connections.

Defining trust in a Relationship: Trust in romance transcends the mere expectation of fidelity. It encompasses the belief in each other's reliability, the transparency of actions and intentions, and the mutual respect for individual boundaries and vulnerabilities. It's the confidence that your partner will act in the best interest of the relationship, even in challenging times.

Trust Breakers vs. Trust Builders: Trust can be fragile, susceptible to erosion by actions as overt as infidelity or as subtle as inconsistency. Betrayals, deceit, and even the failure to support each other in crucial moments can sever the threads of trust. Conversely, trust is fortified through honesty, reliability, emotional support, and the continuous nurturing of the relationship. It's in the daily acts of kindness, understanding, and unwavering belief in one another.

The Role of Reliability and Consistency: Reliability and consistency in actions and words lay the foundation of trust brick by brick, echoing the age-old wisdom that 'actions speak louder than words.' These elements demonstrate predictability in one's behavior, offering security and stability. Consistency between what one does and says is a powerful testament to sincerity and commitment, embodying the principle that 'trust is earned, not given.' Simply put, for a relationship to thrive, it is imperative that each partner truly 'walks the talk.'

Transparency and Openness: Transparency is the window through which the heart's true intentions are seen, and openness allows for the free flow of thoughts and feelings. Together, they create an environment where doubts can be dispelled, and the relationship can thrive on honesty and clarity. Being transparent about one's feelings, desires, and fears and open to discussing them is pivotal in nurturing trust.

Respect and Mutual Understanding: Trust is also deeply rooted in respect for each other's boundaries and a mutual understanding of each other's needs and desires. Recognizing and honoring these boundaries without coercion or resentment speaks volumes of the respect partners hold for each other. This respect, coupled with the effort to understand and empathize with one another, strengthens the trust between partners, enabling them to navigate the complexities of their relationship with confidence and assurance.

48

As we already established, trust is not a given; it's earned and maintained through a continuous commitment to these principles. Understanding and embodying these elements can transform a relationship, creating a bond that is resilient in the face of adversity and capable of deepening and enriching the connection between partners.

Trust-Building Exercises

Building trust is an ongoing journey that requires conscious effort, commitment, and creativity. Whether your relationship is just beginning or has spanned years, you can always deepen and fortify trust. Here are some practical activities designed to reinforce trust between partners.

❦ ❦ ❦ ❦ ❦ ❦❦ ❦

Exercise 1: Daily Trust-Building

Objective: This exercise aims to cultivate a deeper sense of trust and connection between partners through daily practices of vulnerability, openness, and acts of service. By intentionally sharing parts of oneself and performing thoughtful gestures, you will reinforce the foundations of trust in your relationship.

- **Share Daily Discoveries:** Each day this week, make it a point to share something new about yourself with your partner—be it a memory, a thought, or an aspiration. This practice encourages vulnerability and openness.
- **Acts of Service:** Engage in small, thoughtful acts of service for each other. Whether making a cup of coffee in the morning or taking over a chore your partner dislikes, these actions demonstrate care and reliability.
- **Reaffirm Your Bond:** Make a habit of verbally affirming your commitment to each other and the relationship. These affirmations can be expressions of love, commitments to

support each other, or reminders of the trust you've built. Such declarations, especially when made regularly, reinforce the foundation of trust and provide a sense of security and belonging.

Outcome: This exercise strengthens trust, characterized by increased openness and mutual support within the relationship. Over time, these daily practices will enhance your understanding of each other, making the relationship a secure base from which both individuals can grow and flourish. By embedding these habits into your daily routine, you lay the groundwork for a lasting partnership built on a solid foundation of trust.

♥ ♥ ♥ ♥ ♥ ♥♥ ♥

Exercise 2: The Trust Jar

Objective: To create a visible, tangible record of trust-building moments, promoting an atmosphere of gratitude and recognition within the relationship.

Capturing Moments of Trust: Introduce a trust jar into your home, where each of you can drop in notes highlighting moments of appreciation, acts of trust, or times when you felt supported by your partner. At the end of each week, take time together to read through the notes, acknowledging and celebrating these moments. This ritual fosters a culture of appreciation and serves as a tangible reminder of the trust you share.

Outcome: This exercise will culminate in a strengthened sense of partnership and shared history. Reading through the jar's contents weekly allows you to visibly see and appreciate the accumulation of trust and support, reinforcing your security and bond.

❧ ❧ ❧ ❧ ❧ ❧❧ ❧

Exercise 3: Long-Term Trust Projects

Objective: To embark on a joint venture that requires planning, cooperation, and reliability, showcasing the dynamic nature of trust in action through collective goals.

Collaborative Goals: Set up a project you are both passionate about, requiring teamwork and commitment. It could be anything from a home improvement task to planning a trip or taking a class together. The key is that it necessitates cooperation and dependability, strengthening trust through shared achievements. In my experience, couples have embraced various activities as part of this exercise, from enrolling in yoga or dance classes together, dedicating their time to volunteer projects, joining a gym, to pursuing passion projects like writing a book. The possibilities are boundless; this is your chance to embark on something you've long aspired to do together.

Outcome: By undertaking and completing a project together, you will share in the satisfaction of your achievement and the trust and teamwork it took to get there. This shared success will provide a concrete example of your ability to rely on one another, deepening the trust foundation upon which your relationship stands.

❧ ❧ ❧ ❧ ❧ ❧❧ ❧

These activities, from the simplicity of daily gestures to the commitment to long-term projects, offer pathways to strengthen the trust essential to a healthy, thriving relationship. By consciously engaging in these practices, couples can create a robust framework of trust that supports the growth and deepening of their love.

Rebuilding Trust After Betrayal

The journey to rebuild trust after betrayal is one of the most challenging paths a couple can navigate. Yet, with commitment, understanding, and the right strategies, it's possible to emerge stronger on the other side. This section outlines a framework for couples seeking to mend the fabric of their relationship in the aftermath of betrayal.

Acknowledgment and Apology: The first step towards healing is fully acknowledging the betrayal. The person who broke the trust must offer a sincere, unambiguous apology recognizing the specific actions and their detrimental impact. This acknowledgment is crucial, as it validates the feelings of the hurt partner, showing that their pain is understood and taken seriously.

Understanding the Impact: Beyond acknowledgment, it's essential for the betrayer to genuinely comprehend the depth of the impact their actions have had—not just on their partner but on the relationship's foundation itself. This may involve deep, sometimes uncomfortable conversations where the hurt partner shares their feelings of pain, betrayal, and disappointment. It's a process that requires patience, empathy, and a willingness to listen and understand without defensiveness.

Steps to Rebuild Trust: Rebuilding trust is a gradual process that should include concrete steps and, when possible, a timeline. This plan might encompass increased transparency, such as sharing passwords or regular check-ins about one's whereabouts, and efforts to rebuild intimacy, like spending quality time together or engaging in activities that once brought joy to the relationship. Both partners need to be active participants in this process, with the understanding that rebuilding trust takes time and consistent effort.

Seeking External Support: External support can often help on the road to rebuilding trust. Couples therapy, for instance, can offer a neutral space to navigate the complexities of betrayal, providing tools and strategies to facilitate healing. A therapist can help explore the root causes of the betrayal, guide the process of rebuilding trust, and work with the couple to strengthen their communication and emotional connection.

Rebuilding trust after betrayal is a testament to a couple's resilience and commitment to their relationship. It's a process marked by vulnerability, courage, and the shared goal of healing. With dedication to the journey and perhaps guidance from professionals, couples can rediscover trust, intimacy, and a stronger bond than before.

Case Study - Thomas and Mia

Thomas and Mia faced a significant challenge in their relationship due to Thomas's financial infidelity. Thomas had accrued substantial debt without Mia's knowledge, leading to a profound breach of trust when the truth inevitably surfaced. The revelation left Mia feeling betrayed and uncertain about the future of their relationship.

The first step towards healing began with Thomas fully acknowledging the gravity of his actions. He offered Mia a heartfelt apology, acknowledging the pain and mistrust his actions had caused, without attempting to justify or minimize his behavior. This genuine acknowledgment was crucial for Mia to feel heard and validated.

Thomas and Mia's journey through the aftermath of financial infidelity marked a profound period of healing and growth in their relationship. The pivotal moment came when Thomas fully acknowledged his actions and offered Mia a sincere apology, recognizing the pain he had caused without excuses. This act of vulnerability was the first step toward rebuilding the trust that had been shattered.

Guided by the desire to mend their bond, they embarked on a meticulous plan to restore trust. This included Thomas providing complete transparency about their financial status and committing to regular discussions about their financial health and relationship dynamics. They also continued couples therapy, which offered them tailored strategies to navigate their emotions and rebuild intimacy. Through persistent effort, empathy, and professional support, Thomas and Mia gradually rekindled trust and intimacy, transforming their challenge into an opportunity for deeper connection and mutual understanding. Their story underscores the power of sincere acknowledgment, open communication, and a shared commitment to healing.

🖤 🖤 🖤 🖤 🖤 🖤🖤 🖤

Exercise 4: Weekly Trust Check-Ins

Objective: This exercise aims to establish a routine of weekly trust check-ins. This practice aims not just to maintain but to further enrich the trust within your relationship. Think of these check-ins as the ongoing care required for a cherished garden, ensuring that your trust continues to thrive across all seasons of your partnership.

While you are not required to complete a worksheet for this exercise, I've provided a sample set of prompts within the bonus worksheet section to guide your initial Trust Maintenance Check-In. Please take a moment to review these before your first session. You are encouraged to use them as they are or adapt them to better suit your needs.

Initiating Weekly Trust Discussions: Dedicate a moment each week where you come together in a spirit of openness and commitment, creating a sanctuary for trust-related dialogue. This time is sacred, a pause in the hustle of life to connect, reflect, and share your innermost feelings, experiences, and trust concerns. It's about reinforcing the scaffold of your mutual trust, brick by brick, week by week.

Framework for Productive Conversations: Approach these discussions with the goal of understanding and connecting deeply with each other. Engage in active listening, allowing space for each person to share thoughts and feelings uninterrupted. Communicate openly, using "I" statements to express individual experiences and emotions, avoiding blame to create a supportive atmosphere conducive to growth.

Immediately Address Trust Concerns: While the weekly check-ins are invaluable, it's important to feel free to raise trust issues as they arise. Postponing a discussion of concerns until the scheduled check-in can allow wounds to deepen, hindering the healing process. Promptly addressing trust issues as they occur underscores the importance you place on a healthy, trust-filled partnership.

Acknowledging Trust Milestones: Celebrate the significant moments when trust has been strengthened or restored. These acknowledgments are as important as overcoming challenges; they underscore the progress you've made together, reminding you of the durability and depth of your connection.

Outcome: Integrating weekly trust check-ins into your routine will create a dedicated space for open and committed dialogue about trust. This consistent effort is vital maintenance, fortifying the bonds of trust and enabling your relationship to grow stronger and more resilient each week.

Let's shake things up and inject some fun into the serious business of building trust. After all, deepening trust in your relationship doesn't have to be all work and no play. Here's a delightful twist on trust-building activities that promises laughter, joy, and perhaps a little bit of mess—but all in the name of growing closer and strengthening your bond.

♡ ♡ ♡ ♡ ♡ ♡♡ ♡

Exercise 5: Blindfolded Feeding Frenzy

Objective: This game isn't just about food; it's about relying on your partner in a vulnerable yet safe and playful setting. It's a reminder that trust is multifaceted, sometimes requiring us to let go and lean into the experience, guided by our faith in our partner.

Steps:

- Set aside an evening for an activity that's as fun as it is meaningful. The idea here is simple yet profound: one partner is blindfolded and must trust the other to feed them various foods. It's a playful test of trust and surrender, mixed with taste-testing excitement.
- Gather snacks and treats, mixing favorites with a few surprises. The partner doing the feeding guides each bite to the blindfolded partner's mouth, adding elements of suspense and delight with each taste. Remember, the aim is to enjoy the process and each other, not to win a culinary guessing game.
- After one of you is all fed up, swap roles! Once both of you have had a turn, sit down and share your experiences. Talk about what it felt like to be in each position—the feeder and the fed. What did this exercise teach you about trust, vulnerability, and care? Often, it's these light-hearted activities that open up deeper avenues of communication and understanding.

Incorporating activities like the Blindfolded Feeding Frenzy into your weekly trust check-ins brightens the routine. It reinforces the notion that trust is built in moments of vulnerability and care—sometimes, with a spoonful of laughter. So, dive into this playful adventure together and discover the joyous side of building trust.

❦ ❦ ❦ ❦ ❦ ❦❦ ❦

As we conclude Week 4 on the Fundamentals of Trust, we've explored the intricate layers that form the base of every enduring relationship. Through exercises and reflections, we've learned that trust isn't merely about grand gestures; rather, it's cultivated in the daily acts of reliability and the consistency of our words aligning with our actions. This week has underscored the principle that trust, once established, becomes the foundation upon which deeper emotional connections are built, allowing for vulnerability and true intimacy. As we pivot to Week 5, focusing on "Reigniting the Passion" — my favorite week — remember that the trust you've carefully nurtured forms fertile ground for passion to flourish anew. Let's carry forward the commitment to walk our talk, embracing trust not just as a concept, but as the living, breathing essence of our connection.

I WOULD LOVE TO HEAR FROM YOU

If this workbook has enriched your relationship, I kindly ask for your review and for you to share your experience with others. Please take a moment to leave a review on Amazon and share how this book has impacted your connection.

Your feedback not only helps me, but it also guides others on their journey toward deeper connection and emotional health. It's through your endorsements and reviews that we can extend the reach of this book, offering guidance and support to more couples striving for a secure, loving bond.

Please take 60 seconds to kindly leave a review on Amazon.

If you reside outside of US, please use the link in your order.

All it takes is 60 seconds to make a difference!

WEEK 5 - REIGNITING THE PASSION

Welcome to Week 5 of your journey towards a deeper, more vibrant relationship. This week is dedicated to reigniting the passion that initially brought you together. Passion, the intense emotional and physical connection that lights up our relationship, can sometimes dim under the pressures of daily life, communication gaps, and unresolved conflicts. However, the good news is that you can reignite this spark, and throughout this week, I will guide you through a series of steps based on the principles of EFT to achieve just that.

Passion in a relationship is not just about physical intimacy; it's deeply rooted in emotional closeness, understanding, and the ability to express and fulfill desires and needs. This week, we will explore how to deepen your emotional connection, communicate your desires more openly, and embrace physical closeness to enhance your relationship's vitality. You can reignite the passion that fuels your bond through intentional practice and heartfelt communication.

Emotional Disconnect and Its Impact on Passion

Every relationship faces challenges that can lead to moments of emotional disconnection. Whether it's stress from work, the routine of daily life, or unresolved issues, these moments can accumulate, leading to a decrease in passion. Emotional disconnection makes maintaining the closeness necessary for a passionate relationship difficult. Recognizing and addressing these moments not as failures but as opportunities for growth and more profound connection is essential.

Throughout my years of experience, I've had the privilege of working with a diverse array of couples, from life partners whose love for each other is as deep as the ocean to those who navigate the complexities of a polyamorous lifestyle. Each relationship, with its unique blend of challenges and joys, has taught me something profound: At the heart of it all, if all partners are genuinely committed to change, to reigniting that special spark that brought them together, miracles can happen. It doesn't matter the shape or form of the relationship; what matters is the willingness to dive deep together into the journey of reconnection. It's a beautiful, often challenging adventure, but for those ready to rekindle their unique bond, the path is always there, waiting to be rediscovered and cherished anew.

It's important to pause here and share why this week holds a special place in my heart. It addresses an issue nearly every couple brings up early in our sessions: a sense of sexual unfulfillment within their current relationship dynamics. This concern transcends relationship structures, as vividly illustrated by a conversation with a man living in a loving polycule with his three beautiful partners. His openness and vulnerability in sharing this challenge drove home an essential truth: this kind of disconnect can touch any of us, no matter how deep our love for our partners may run. Yet, I remain ever-optimistic. With genuine commitment, concerted effort, and a dash of open-mindedness, navigating through these waters to rediscover passion is entirely within reach. It's a journey of reconnection that, I've found, can bring couples closer than they've ever been.

Reflecting on Emotional Presence

• Take a moment to reflect on your relationship. Can you identify times when you felt particularly disconnected? What was happening in your lives at that time?

• Consider how this disconnection affected your emotional intimacy and physical closeness.

Expressing Desires and Needs

Communicating your innermost desires and needs is vulnerable but essential for maintaining a strong and passionate relationship. This week, we will introduce strategies to help you feel safe and supported in expressing yourself. Learning to articulate what you truly want and need from each other can transform your relationship, creating a foundation of trust and mutual understanding that reignites passion.

Begin to think about what you most desire from your partner physically, emotionally, and spiritually. How do these desires support your vision for a passionate relationship?

The Role of Physical Intimacy in Emotional Connection

The connection between emotional intimacy and physical closeness is undeniable. Physical intimacy, from a tender touch to a loving gaze, reinforces the emotional bond you share, adding depth and excitement to your relationship. Let's start this week by exploring how to integrate physical expressions of love into your daily interactions, using them as a bridge to deeper emotional intimacy.

❧ ❧ ❧ ❧ ❧ ❧❧ ❧

Exercise 1: Desire Mapping

Objective: To create a safe and open space for couples to explore and articulate their deepest desires, both emotional and physical. This exercise aims to foster a deeper understanding and empathy between partners, enabling them to express their needs more clearly and confidently.

Steps:

1. **Preparation:** Set time aside so each partner has a quiet, comfortable space without distractions. Equip yourselves with writing materials of your choice — a journal or sheets of paper and pens. Do not use an electronic device for writing if you might get distracted by it. The goal is to dedicate this time to your relationship. If you are too timid to put words on paper, I have heard a glass of wine or another choice beverage could help.

2. **Parallel Reflection:** Separately, spend about 15 minutes reflecting on your desires within the relationship. Consider all aspects—emotional, physical, intellectual, and spiritual. Think about what makes you feel loved, connected, and fulfilled.

3. **Writing Down Your Desires:** Write your reflections in clear, concise statements. Aim for honesty and openness without fear of judgment. This is your safe space to express your true self. You might have already noticed that I've chosen not to provide a worksheet for this exercise. Experience has shown that in certain situations, embracing a less structured approach can significantly enhance the effectiveness of the exercise. This method allows couples to engage more freely and authentically, fostering deeper connections without the constraints of a predefined format. The flexibility of this exercise encourages open, spontaneous dialogue, which is often where the most meaningful breakthroughs occur. Trust in this process and in each other as you explore this journey together.

4. **Sharing:** Come back together and, one at a time, share your desires with your partner. As you share, the listener should practice active listening—acknowledging without interrupting, offering empathy, and striving to understand deeply.

5. **Discussion:** After both have shared, discuss your thoughts and feelings about what you've learned from each other. Identify any common desires or areas where you can grow together. Discuss how you might support each other in fulfilling these desires.
6. **Action Plan:** Together, choose one or two desires each to focus on in the coming weeks. Develop a simple, actionable plan for how you will address these desires. This might involve scheduling regular date nights, dedicating time to talk about your day, or exploring new activities together.

Outcome: By the end of the Desire Mapping exercise, you will achieve a deeper mutual understanding and appreciation of each other's desires. This exercise paves the way for more open, honest communication and lays the groundwork for meeting each other's needs more effectively. Ultimately, the Desire Mapping exercise is about bridging the gap between longing and fulfillment, leading to a more connected and satisfying relationship.

❦ ❦ ❦ ❦ ❦ ❦❦ ❦

Cultivating Daily Intimacy

Reflect on the role of physical intimacy in your relationship. How does it express the emotional bond you share? Are there barriers that prevent you from expressing this form of intimacy?

As we progress through this week, remember that reigniting passion is a journey, not a destination. It requires patience, understanding, and a willingness to explore the depths of your relationship. By committing to this process, you're taking a significant step towards a more fulfilling and passionate partnership.

♥ ♥ ♥ ♥ ♥ ♥♥ ♥

Exercise 2: Intimacy Rituals Creation

Objective: The Intimacy Rituals Creation exercise is designed to help you establish meaningful, regular practices that cultivate emotional and physical intimacy. The objective is to identify activities both partners find nurturing, comforting, and connective and turn these into consistent rituals. These rituals reinforce your bond, ensuring that acts of love and connection become integral parts of their daily lives.

Steps:

1. **Brainstorming Session:** Begin with a collaborative brainstorming session where both partners suggest activities that make them feel loved, valued, and connected. Consider a range of activities, from simple gestures like holding hands during a walk to more elaborate plans like weekly date nights or weekend getaways.

2. **Reflect on Preferences:** Discuss each suggestion, reflecting on how it aligns with your individual and shared preferences. Consider the practicality of integrating these activities into your daily or weekly routines.

3. **Selecting Rituals:** Choose several activities (aim for a mix of simple daily rituals and more significant weekly or monthly ones) that you both feel enthusiastic about. Aim for diversity to keep the rituals exciting and fulfilling.

4. **Detailing Your Rituals:** For each selected activity, outline the specifics—when, where, and how often it will occur. The more detailed your plan, the easier it will be to follow through.

5. **Commitment Discussion:** Have an open conversation about the importance of these rituals in strengthening your relationship. Acknowledge the effort and commitment required from both sides to make these rituals a consistent part of your life.

6. **Make It Happen:** We all know life gets in the way, so create a shared calendar or set reminders for your chosen rituals. Incorporate this into your weekly check-in to discuss how the rituals are going, what adjustments might be needed, and how they impact your relationship.

Outcome: The Intimacy Rituals Creation exercise is designed to culminate in shared practices that both of you look forward to, reinforcing your emotional and physical connection. By intentionally incorporating these rituals into your lives, you can ensure that your relationship remains a priority, fostering a more profound sense of unity and satisfaction. Over time, these rituals become cherished aspects of the relationship, symbols of love and commitment that nurture the partnership's growth and resilience.

🐦 🐦 🐦 🐦 🐦 🐦🐦 🐦

Exercise 3: Guided Exploration

Objective: This exercise, deeply rooted in EFT principles, aims to enhance emotional connection and trust between partners through the power of touch and verbal expression of desires. This guided experience fosters vulnerability and closeness, serving as a pathway to rekindle passion and intimacy.

Get Ready to Explore:

1. **Set the Scene:** Create a comfortable, private space free from distractions. Soften the lighting, perhaps with candles or dim lights, and ensure a comfortable seating area for the partner on the receiving end of this exploratory journey. Have a blindfold ready, along with any soft fabrics or items you might use for a gentle touch. Keep in mind that the tools for this journey need not be elaborate. Often, the simplest household items can transform into instruments of profound sensation. A plush stuffed toy, the unexpected coolness of a metal belt

buckle can offer surprisingly intense experiences when wielded with intention, especially for a partner whose sight is temporarily shielded. For those familiar with the nuanced depth of 'Scent of a Woman' featuring Al Pacino, imagine the heightened senses and the anticipation of the unknown, illustrating how everyday objects can become extraordinary in the right context.

2. **Blindfold:** One partner puts on the blindfold and sits comfortably, ready to receive touch. The other partner takes the role of the explorer. The blindfolded partner should focus on breathing deeply and remaining present in the moment. Remember that by incorporating a blindfold, the exercise intensifies the sense of touch and hearing, encouraging partners to communicate and connect more profoundly.

3. **Guided Touch:** The exploring partner gently touches the blindfolded partner. Start with non-sexual areas, such as the arms, hands, face, and hair, gradually moving to more intimate areas as comfort and consent are established. Use a variety of textures and touches, paying close attention to the blindfolded partner's reactions and comfort levels.

4. **Whispering Desires:** As the exploring partner touches, they also whisper their desires to the blindfolded partner. These can be specific acts of intimacy they enjoy, traits they admire about their partner or fantasies they wish to share. The key is to express these desires gently and lovingly, creating a safe space for vulnerability.

5. **Feedback and Sharing:** After the exercise, switch roles, ensuring each of you can experience being both the explorer and the one being explored. Following the exercise, partners remove the blindfold and share their experiences, focusing on what they felt, discovered, and enjoyed.

6. **Reflecting Together:** Engage in a conversation about how the exercise impacted your emotional connection. Discuss any new insights into each other's desires and how you can integrate this deeper understanding into your relationship.

Outcome: The Guided Exploration exercise is designed to deepen trust and emotional intimacy, critical components of EFT, by engaging the senses and encouraging vulnerable communication. This experience can help partners feel more connected, understood, and desired, laying a foundation for enhanced intimacy and passion. Through such exercises, you learn to navigate your emotional landscapes with sensitivity and awareness, strengthening your bond and reigniting the spark that brings you together.

I have observed wonderfully diverse outcomes of this exercise, with some partners sharing a moment of uncontrollable laughter after a softly whispered joke. In contrast, others have found themselves reconnecting through a night filled with passion and intimacy. Regardless of your initial outcome, it's vital to recognize the significant step you've taken toward reigniting your relationship's spark. By dedicating time, venturing beyond your comfort zones, and engaging in this activity together, you've laid the groundwork for deeper connection and affection.

As you reflect on this experience, consider taking it a bit further by contemplating the depths of vulnerability you're willing to explore with your partner. Ask yourself: How much trust and control am I prepared to offer and accept? How open am I to receive? These questions pave the way for profound discussions and insights, further strengthening the bonds of your relationship.

❦ ❦ ❦ ❦ ❦ ❦❦ ❦

Exercise 4: Bring It UP a Notch

Now, imagine you would like to take your guided exploration a bit further and are ready to explore giving and taking a bit more.

1. **Get Ready:** Begin by establishing a foundation of mutual consent and understanding. Discuss the idea of incorporating symbolic gestures that represent trust and vulnerability within your exploration. If both partners are comfortable, choose a symbol of trust, such as a soft fabric that loosely represents the idea of binding (a necktie you no longer wear would be perfect).

2. **Bind:** Symbolically bind your partner's hands in a position that doesn't cause discomfort or strain, especially for those who are new to such explorations. The bind should be gentle and easily removable at any point, prioritizing comfort and safety in a position that doesn't cause discomfort or strain.

3. **Explore:** Proceed with a guided exploration, building on the principles of openness and sensitivity discussed in the earlier exercise. Remember that the partner taking on a symbolic gesture of vulnerability by being bound and blindfolded will have every sensation and experience amplified. It's crucial to remain attuned to each other's responses and emotions, maintaining a nurturing and respectful environment. Continue being present and responsive to your partner's reactions to foster a safe and positive experience.

4. **Switch:** Switch roles and see how it feels on the other side of the trust equation. Switching roles to experience the dynamics of trust from both perspectives can deepen understanding and empathy within the relationship, highlighting the importance of mutual support and consent.

5. **Feedback and Sharing:** Take time to reflect on and share your experiences together. Discuss your feelings around trust and

the responsibility of care you held for each other. This step is vital for reinforcing your connection and ensuring that both partners feel heard and valued.

Outcome: This exercise is designed to enrich the bonds of trust and intimacy between partners. Drawing inspiration from the time-honored art of rope bondage, it offers a unique pathway to explore the depths of your connection. Should this experience spark a deeper interest in discovering new dimensions of trust and closeness through rope bondage, I encourage you to check out "The Art of Shibari" by That Rope Guy. This book serves as a comprehensive guide, inviting you to delve further into the intricate and meaningful practice of Shibari, enhancing your journey towards mutual understanding and intimacy.

♡ ♡ ♡ ♡ ♡ ♡♡ ♡

Addressing Desire Discrepancies Compassionately

It's essential to start by recognizing that variations in sexual desire within a relationship are entirely normal. These discrepancies often stem from differences in individual physiology, emotional needs, stress levels, and experiences. Embracing this understanding lays a foundation for approaching the subject with compassion and empathy. Remember, acknowledging these differences does not signify incompatibility; rather, it highlights the unique tapestry of your relationship.

Communicating About Desires

Open and sensitive communication about desires and needs is pivotal in any relationship. Here's a step-by-step strategy to foster a supportive dialogue:

- **Choose the Right Moment:** Initiate the conversation at a time when both partners feel relaxed and open, away from stressors and distractions.
- **Use "I" Statements:** Express your feelings and needs by starting sentences with "I" to avoid making your partner feel defensive.
- **Listen Actively:** When your partner speaks, listen to understand, not to respond. Validate their feelings even if you see things differently.
- **Express Empathy:** Show empathy towards your partner's desires and concerns. Let them know that their feelings are valid and important to you.

Finding Mutual Satisfaction

Achieving mutual satisfaction involves finding creative solutions and compromises that honor both partners' needs. This journey is about exploration and flexibility, not just concession. Here are strategies to guide you:

Explore New Avenues Together

Exploring new avenues together requires an open-minded approach to intimacy, where both partners feel comfortable expressing their desires and boundaries. Begin by establishing a dialogue that invites honest and vulnerable communication about your intimate needs and fantasies. This can involve discussing things you've both wanted to try but perhaps felt hesitant to bring up. Whether experimenting with new positions, incorporating toys, or exploring tantric practices, the key is approaching these discussions with curiosity and an open heart.

As you embark on this journey, remember to maintain a sense of playfulness and adventure. It's not just about the act itself but about deepening your connection and understanding of each other's desires. Finding mutual satisfaction may involve trying things that don't initially appeal to you but could be a source of joy for your partner. In these moments, compassion and compromise become your guides. Navigating these new experiences together fosters an environment where both partners feel seen, heard, and satisfied.

Prioritize Emotional Intimacy: Strengthening your emotional connection can enhance your sexual and romantic relationship. This entails dedicating time and effort to truly connect on an emotional level beyond the surface interactions of daily life. Spending quality time together, engaging in meaningful conversations, sharing personal dreams and fears, and actively listening to each other can significantly enhance your bond. Embarking on this 8-week journey together, you've already laid a solid foundation of playfulness and mutual exploration, enriching both your emotional and intimate connections. As you transition into prioritizing emotional intimacy, remember that you're already halfway through this transformative journey, having navigated 19 exercises together over the last four weeks. This remarkable progress is a testament to your commitment and the depth of your bond. By continuing to explore new experiences and deepen your emotional intimacy, you're not just enhancing your relationship; you're fortifying and enriching your connection.

💕 💕 💕 💕 💕 💕💕 💕

Exercise 5: Desire Discovery Dialogue

This exercise involves both partners listing sexual activities they are interested in under the "yes," "no," or "maybe" categories. It's a practical tool to understand and respect each other's boundaries while exploring mutual interests.

I've consciously decided against providing a predefined starter list in the accompanying worksheets. The reason is straightforward yet profound: the most effective practices and boundaries are those defined by you and your partner together. As we're aware, an activity that one person considers routine might be entirely off-limits for another. Therefore, it's crucial that your list incorporates suggestions and perspectives from both of you for each proposed activity. To facilitate clear communication, the list should include a dedicated column for each partner — Partner 1 and Partner 2 — with options of "yes," "no," or "maybe" indicated for every activity. This approach ensures a mutual understanding and respect for each other's boundaries and preferences.

In exploring areas of mutual curiosity, engage in open dialogue to determine, without any pressure, what conditions would make both partners comfortable transitioning a "maybe" into a "yes." Discuss and understand the underlying reasons for each other's hesitations or concerns. Why does a partner feel hesitant about a certain activity? What needs or fears are influencing their perspective? This conversation is an opportunity to deepen your connection by revealing vulnerabilities and preferences. It's about creating a safe space where both partners feel heard and respected, enabling you to navigate your boundaries with empathy and understanding.

❦ ❦ ❦ ❦ ❦ ❦❦ ❦

Case Study - Jamie and Morgan

Jamie had carried a silent curiosity about exploring beyond the traditional boundaries of his relationship with Morgan for several years, specifically, he found himself contemplating the inclusion of a third partner or the possibility of a threesome. This curiosity wasn't born out of dissatisfaction but from a desire to explore new dimensions of their connection and intimacy. This unspoken thought became a source of internal conflict for Jamie, creating a subtle yet growing sense of dissatisfaction that seemed to cast a shadow over their otherwise harmonious partnership. Despite the strength of their connection, Jamie's fear of Morgan's potential reaction — and the possible impact on their relationship — kept this curiosity buried deep, unvoiced, and unexplored.

The turning point arrived when Jamie and Morgan sought my guidance, initially to address what they described as an 'unidentifiable strain' affecting their bond. Through the "Desire Discovery Dialogue," an exercise designed to foster open, vulnerable communication, Jamie found the courage to unveil his long-held curiosity. This revelation was a pivotal moment, not only for Jamie in expressing their truth but for Morgan, who faced this unexpected insight into Jamie's inner world for the first time.

Morgan's response, facilitated by the structured, empathetic environment of the dialogue, was to listen with an open heart, shifting from surprise to understanding. This exercise proved to be a crucial step in transforming their relationship. It opened up a space for Morgan to consider perspectives they had never imagined, fostering a more profound emotional intimacy between them. The dialogue laid the groundwork for Jamie and Morgan to explore this new dimension of their relationship together, moving from a place of fear and dissatisfaction to one of mutual curiosity and deeper connection. Through this journey, they learned the importance of vulnerability and clear communication, illustrating that even deeply held fears and desires can be navigated successfully with trust and open dialogue.

This case study underscores the transformative power of vulnerability and communication in relationships. Jamie and Morgan's experience highlights how addressing unspoken thoughts and fears can resolve underlying tensions and open up new avenues for growth and connection within a partnership.

Professional Support

While the strategies outlined above can significantly help, there may be times when professional guidance is necessary. Therapists and counselors specializing in EFT can provide invaluable support in navigating desire discrepancies. They offer a safe space to explore sensitive topics, equip couples with communication strategies, and work through underlying issues affecting their sexual relationship.

Remember, seeking professional help is a sign of strength and commitment to your relationship's health. It's about growing together, understanding each other's needs, and fostering a secure, satisfying bond.

Wrapping up Week 5, you've both dived deep and soared high, reigniting flames of passion and intimacy that perhaps you hadn't felt in a while—or maybe ever discovered until now. This week was about embarking on an adventure together, trying things off the beaten path, and rediscovering each other in new, exciting ways. The laughter, closeness, and sheer fun of exploring together are the moments that build the bedrock of your relationship. As you gear up for Week 6, "Navigating Conflicts with Compassion," carry with you the spirit of adventure and the joy of your discoveries. Let the excitement of what you've experienced fuel your journey forward. The resilience, understanding, and connection you've forged this week are the very tools that will empower you to face and resolve conflicts with empathy and strength. With each step forward, you're not just moving through exercises; you're crafting a richer, deeper bond, ready to embrace the challenges and joys ahead.

WEEK 6 - NAVIGATING CONFLICT WITH COMPASSION

Welcome to Week 6, where our journey takes a profound turn towards transforming how we engage with conflict in our relationships. Often perceived as a source of tension, conflict holds a hidden opportunity for growth, intimacy, and strengthening the bonds between partners when navigated with care and empathy. This week, we will delve into the art of navigating conflicts with compassion, a pivotal skill for couples aiming to build a resilient, deeply connected relationship. Through exploring principles and practices designed to approach disagreements constructively, we embark on a path where conflicts become not battles to win but opportunities for mutual understanding and growth. Let's set forth on this enlightening journey, transforming moments of discord into milestones of connection and understanding.

The Compassionate Conflict Blueprint

This section explores the transformative power of handling disagreements with care and understanding. Conflicts, inevitable in every relationship, carry the potential for growth and deepening bonds when approached with compassion. Herein lies a blueprint for engaging in disputes not as adversaries but as partners eager to understand and support each other.

Principles of Compassionate Conflict

- **Empathy:** The cornerstone of compassionate conflict is the ability to understand and share your partner's feelings genuinely. It means seeing beyond your perspective to appreciate the situation from their eyes.
- **Patience:** Conflict resolution is not a race to the finish line. It requires time and patience to comprehend each other's views and emotions fully. Patience fosters a calm, supportive environment conducive to mutual understanding.
- **Openness:** Keeping an open mind allows for considering new ideas and perspectives. It paves the way for innovative solutions catering to both partners' well-being.

By adhering to these principles, couples can transform conflict from a source of stress into an opportunity for strengthening their relationship.

Steps to Compassionate Conflict Resolution

- **Initiate with a Positive Intent:** Begin the discussion with affirmations of love and respect. This sets a constructive tone for the conversation.
- **Active Listening:** Listen not just to respond but to understand. Acknowledge your partner's feelings and perspectives without judgment.
- **Affirm and Validate:** Express validation by acknowledging the validity of your partner's emotions and viewpoints, even if you don't entirely agree. This shows respect for their experience.
- **Express Your Feelings:** Share your emotions and needs honestly but gently. Use "I" statements to communicate your feelings without blaming your partner.

- **Seek Common Ground:** Identify mutual goals and values that both of you agree on. This shared foundation can guide you toward resolutions that honor both partners' needs.
- **Develop Solutions Together:** Brainstorm solutions that address both partners' concerns. Compromise and creativity are vital in finding a path forward that enriches your relationship.
- **Affirm Commitment:** Conclude by reaffirming your commitment to each other and the relationship. Recognize the effort to navigate conflict with compassion and celebrate the progress made.

The Role of Self-Compassion

Self-compassion is essential in conflict resolution. It involves treating yourself with the same kindness, concern, and understanding you would offer a good friend. Recognizing your own emotional needs and granting yourself grace during challenging times not only aids in personal well-being but also in the capacity to engage empathetically with your partner.

Developing a Conflict Resolution Plan

Creating a personalized conflict resolution plan enables couples to approach disagreements confidently and clearly. This plan should:

- **Identify Trigger Points:** Recognize situations or topics likely to spark conflict. Understanding these triggers allows for proactive measures to approach them thoughtfully.
- **Set Guidelines for Engagement:** Agree on fair and respectful communication rules. This might include no yelling, taking turns speaking, or implementing a "time-out" when emotions run high.
- **Choose a Safe Space:** Designate a peaceful discussion setting where both partners feel comfortable and secure.

- **Decide on a Signal for Pause:** Sometimes, a break is needed to cool down and collect thoughts. Agree on a signal that either partner can use to pause the conversation respectfully.
- **Commit to Regular Check-Ins:** Schedule times to discuss the health of your relationship, including how effectively you're managing conflicts. These check-ins encourage continuous growth and adaptation.

❧ ❧ ❧ ❧ ❧ ❧❧ ❧

Exercise 1 - Conflict Resolution Plan

Objective: Cultivate a compassionate approach to conflict that resolves disagreements and fosters deeper connection and understanding.

See Worksheet

Steps:

- Leverage the provided blueprint to craft a personalized conflict resolution plan tailored to your relationship's unique dynamics. This book includes a printable template designed to serve as a dynamic, evolving framework for your plan.
- As you progress and discover which strategies effectively resonate within your partnership, integrate discussions on these successes and challenges into your weekly check-ins. The resolution plan is meant to be flexible, encouraging you to amend and evolve it as needed. Celebrate these adjustments by completing a new template version and renewing your commitment to constructive, loving conflict resolution.

Outcome: By embracing this Conflict Resolution Plan, couples will not only navigate conflicts with greater understanding and empathy but also emerge with a strengthened bond, fostering a deeper, more resilient connection. It's a commitment to transforming challenges into opportunities for growth and deeper intimacy within the relationship.

Exercise 2: Empathy in Action Role-Play

Objective: These activities are designed to cultivate a deeper comprehension and articulation of each other's perspectives, particularly in conflict situations, fostering a more empathetic and connected partnership.

Instructions:

1. **Empathy-Building Role-Play:** Select a conflict scenario to role-play, with one partner sharing their perspective. Detail emotions and thoughts as the situation unfolds.
2. **Switching Perspectives:** Switch roles; each partner now adopts the other's viewpoint, aiming to accurately convey their partner's emotional state and perspective.
3. **Using Empathy Statements:** Identify and incorporate empathy statements that would have been beneficial during the conflict. Practice using these statements within the role-play.
4. **Reflecting on the Role of Empathy:** Engage in a reflective discussion on the exercise's impact, focusing on insights gained, feelings experienced while embodying the other's perspective, and the effect of empathy statements on the conflict's emotional tone.
5. **Reflection and Integration:** Close the exercise with a moment for personal reflection and a discussion on actionable steps to integrate the insights gained into daily interactions. This should include strategies for employing empathy in future conflicts to foster a more understanding and supportive relationship dynamic.

Outcome: Upon completion of this exercise, partners will enhance their emotional attunement and responsiveness, core elements of EFT, leading to a significant improvement in their ability to navigate conflicts with empathy and understanding. This approach fosters a more secure attachment and strengthens the bond between partners, turning challenges into opportunities for connection.

❦ ❦ ❦ ❦ ❦ ❦❦ ❦

Re-framing Conflict: A New Perspective

In our journey together, we've explored the intricacies of engaging with conflict through a lens of compassion and understanding. Now, we venture into the transformative realm of re-framing conflict, shifting from viewing it as a source of stress to recognizing it as a fertile ground for growth and connection.

Conflicts are often perceived as negative experiences that threaten the harmony of a relationship. This perspective, however, overlooks the inherent potential conflicts hold for fostering deeper understanding, intimacy, and personal growth. By challenging this narrative and viewing conflict as an opportunity, we open the door to transformative experiences that can strengthen the bonds between partners.

Re-framing Techniques

Re-framing involves altering the way we perceive and interpret conflicts, focusing on the positive aspects and opportunities they present. Techniques include:

- **Looking for the Lesson:** Each conflict offers a lesson or insight into ourselves, our partner, or our relationship. Ask, "What can we learn from this experience?"
- **Identifying Growth Opportunities:** Consider how navigating this conflict can contribute to your personal development or the growth of your relationship.
- **Shifting Focus:** Instead of dwelling on the negative, focus on potential positive outcomes, like enhanced communication skills or a deeper understanding of each other's needs.

The Impact of Positive Re-framing on Resolution

Positive re-framing can significantly alter the course of conflict resolution. By approaching disagreements with an open mind and a focus on growth, couples are more likely to find creative, satisfying solutions that address the needs of both partners. This approach encourages a collaborative rather than adversarial mindset, leading to resolutions that strengthen the relationship.

Exercise 3 - Practice Re-framing in Real Conflicts

Objective: The true test of re-framing lies in its application to real-life conflicts. Turn your recent challenge into a catalyst for connection and insight.

1. **Identify a Recent Conflict:** Choose a disagreement that occurred recently or one that is ongoing.
2. **Apply Re-framing Techniques:** Use the abovementioned techniques to alter your perception of the conflict. Look for lessons, growth opportunities, and positive aspects.
3. **Reflect on the Outcome:** After applying these techniques, discuss as a couple how the re-framing impacted your approach to the conflict and its resolution. Consider changes in emotions, attitudes, and the final result.

Outcome: This exercise is not just about resolving a single disagreement but about cultivating a mindset that views conflicts as chances to enhance connection, understanding, and growth within the relationship. As you practice re-framing, you'll find that what once seemed like obstacles can become stepping stones to a deeper, more resilient bond.

Preventing and Managing Future Conflicts

In the journey of a relationship, foresight and preparedness can transform potential conflicts from stumbling blocks into stepping stones for growth. This section delves into strategies for recognizing early signs of discontent and proactively addressing them, as well as navigating future conflicts with wisdom and empathy.

Early Warning Signs of Discontent

Identifying Red Flags: Couples must become fluent in the language of their relationship's subtle signals. Learning to recognize early warning signs—such as decreased communication, irritation over minor issues, or withdrawal—can alert partners to underlying matters needing attention.

Open Communication Channels: Open, honest communication is the backbone of a healthy relationship. Emphasizing the importance of discussing concerns as they arise prevents minor issues from escalating into major conflicts.

Preventative Measures: Proactive communication strategies, engaging in shared activities that strengthen the bond, and regular check-ins about the relationship's health are all preventative measures that can address early signs of discontent.

Creating a Safe Space for Expression: Cultivating an environment where both partners feel secure to voice their feelings and concerns without fear of judgment or reprisal is essential. This safety net encourages timely and honest communication.

Navigating Conflict with Future Foresight

Anticipating Potential Conflicts: By analyzing past conflicts and current relationship dynamics, couples can become adept at foreseeing potential future disagreements. This foresight allows for preemptive strategies to mitigate or avoid these conflicts.

Preparatory Communication: Engaging in discussions about potential future conflicts in a calm, non-confrontational manner equips both partners with the understanding and tools needed to navigate them more effectively when they arise.

Developing Conflict Resolution Skills: It is vital to develop skills such as negotiation, compromise, and especially empathy on an ongoing basis. These skills are not static but grow through practice and reflection, enabling couples to handle future conflicts with greater ease and understanding.

🖤 🖤 🖤 🖤 🖤 🖤🖤 🖤

Exercise 4: The Future Letter

Objective: This unique exercise encourages you to address present conflicts with a forward-thinking mindset, focusing on compassion, understanding, and the shared future you wish to build. It combines empa-  thy, perspective-taking, and long-term goal-setting to navigate current disagreements.

See Worksheet

Description:

Conflicts often become mired in the immediate emotions and details of the situation, losing sight of the bigger picture and long-term implications for the relationship. The Future Letter exercise helps couples step out of the current moment and consider their future selves and relationships, fostering a broader perspective that can diffuse the intensity of present disagreements.

Steps:

1. **Separate Reflection:** Individually, each partner takes some quiet time to imagine their relationship three years from now, focusing on the positive outcomes they hope to achieve together. Consider what you have overcome, the strength of your bond, and the joy of your partnership. I have included a prompted worksheet you can use to help you reflect and draft your letter.

2. **Writing the Letter:** Each partner writes a letter to themselves from the perspective of three years in the future. This letter should reflect on the current conflict and describe how it was resolved, emphasizing the growth, understanding, and compassion that emerged from the experience. Detail the positive impact resolving this conflict had on the relationship.

3. **Sharing and Discussion:** Partners take turns reading their letters to each other. Listen actively and with an open heart to your partner's vision of the future. After sharing, discuss the common themes in your letters. What hopes and outcomes do you share? How did each of you envision overcoming the current conflict?

4. **Actionable Steps:** Together, identify actionable steps you can take now to begin moving towards the future described in your letters. These should include ways to address the current conflict with compassion and understanding.

5. **Commitment to the Future:** Conclude the exercise by making a commitment to each other to take the identified steps. Consider keeping the letters in a place where they can be revisited as a reminder of your shared goals and the compassionate approach you wish to maintain.

Outcome: The Future Letter exercise aims to shift the focus from winning the current argument to building a future together founded on mutual respect, understanding, and love. It serves as a reminder that conflicts while challenging, are opportunities for growth and deeper connection when approached with a compassionate and long-term perspective.

Case Study - Andy and Tamara

When Andy and Tamara, a dynamic duo caught in the city's never-ending buzz, found themselves spiraling into a vortex of stress-driven spats, they knew something had to give. Juggling the high stakes of Andy's tech world and Tamara's cutthroat public relations scene, their workday woes began to seep into their home life, sparking fires of conflict that neither knew how to extinguish. They reached out to me in search of a lifeline, eager to rediscover harmony within their relationship chaos.

As their life coach, I introduced them to the concept of recognizing early warning signs of conflict, an approach grounded in the teachings of "Navigating Conflict with Compassion." Together, we worked on identifying the subtle cues that preceded their disagreements, such as shortness of breath, avoidance behavior, or snappy replies over minor issues. With this newfound awareness, Andy and Tamara committed to implementing daily rituals aimed at preventing these sparks from igniting into larger conflicts. They embraced nightly discussions, a time dedicated solely to sharing their day's highs and lows, which became a sacred space for connection and empathy. This simple yet profound practice allowed them to address potential issues proactively, strengthening their bond and understanding. Through this process, Andy and Tamara learned not just to manage their conflicts but to transform them into opportunities for growth, marking a significant shift in their relationship dynamics. Their story is a testament to the power of early intervention and the importance of cultivating daily rituals of connection to break the cycle of conflict and foster a deeper, more resilient partnership.

With the guidance on how to navigate conflict with compassion, they learned to recognize the subtle signals preceding their clashes—those critical moments when a deep breath was more of a sigh and silence spoke volumes. Armed with this awareness, Andy and Tamara embarked on a mission to preempt the disagreements that had become their norm. They instituted an evening ritual, carving out a sacred moment amidst the chaos to exchange stories of triumphs and trials from their day. This wasn't just small talk; it was their bridge back to each other, a way to defuse tensions before they escalated. This shift from reactive to proactive, from battling to understanding, didn't just change how they dealt with conflict—it transformed their relationship. Andy and Tamara's journey from discord to deeper connection underscores the transformative potential of tuning into the early whispers of conflict and the power of daily rituals in forging unbreakable bonds.

The Role of Rituals in Preventing Conflicts

Rituals, those repeated actions imbued with intention and meaning, play a pivotal role in any relationship. They go beyond simple routines to actively fortify connections, enhancing the bond and promoting unity and understanding. In terms of preventing conflicts, these rituals serve a dual purpose: they soothe existing tensions and guide us toward a shared future with clarity and purpose.

Establishing Connection Rituals

The importance of establishing daily or weekly rituals that nurture connection and facilitate open communication cannot be overstated. Whether it's a morning coffee shared in silence, an evening walk, or a weekly date night, these rituals become sacred moments of togetherness. They create a consistent space for partners to connect, share, and listen to each other, laying a foundation that can significantly reduce the likelihood of misunderstandings and conflicts.

Rituals for Reconnection

Disagreements and periods of distance are inevitable in any relationship, but rituals for reconnection can help bridge these gaps. These might include a specific activity that both partners enjoy, a way of apologizing that holds special meaning, or a quiet moment of recommitment to each other. Such rituals act as a reset button, signaling a willingness to move beyond conflict and reaffirm the connection.

Customizing Rituals

Each relationship is as unique as the individuals within it, and so, too, should be their rituals. Couples are encouraged to engage in a creative process of defining what rituals resonate most with them. This customization ensures that the rituals are not only enjoyable but also deeply meaningful and effective in strengthening their bond.

The Preventative Power of Rituals

Engaging in regular, meaningful rituals serves as a powerful preventative measure against conflict. By maintaining a strong emotional bond, these rituals ensure that partners remain attuned to each other's needs and feelings. They create a regular cadence of connection that keeps the lines of communication open, making it easier to address issues promptly before they escalate into larger conflicts.

In essence, the role of rituals in preventing conflicts underscores the profound impact of intentional, repeated actions on a relationship's health and longevity. By cultivating these sacred practices, couples can fortify their bond, navigate challenges gracefully, and foster a lasting connection that thrives on understanding and love.

Exercise 5: Time Capsule for Connection and Conflict Prevention

Objective: This exercise invites you to create a time capsule that encapsulates your current feelings, hopes, and shared dreams, with a specific focus on strengthening their relation-

ship and preventing future conflicts. By reflecting on your bond and envisioning your future together, you will reinforce your commitment to each other and establish a foundation for navigating challenges collaboratively.

Steps:

Gather Materials: Select items that represent your relationship's present state and your aspirations for the future. These can include photographs, letters to each other, favorite songs, and symbols of shared goals or dreams.

Write Letters: Each partner writes a letter to their future selves and one to their partner. In these letters, reflect on your current feelings, express your hopes for your relationship, and discuss how you envision overcoming challenges together. Mention your partner's strengths and the relationship and how these can be a foundation for resolving future conflicts. For those of you who aren't big on writing letters, don't worry! I've put together a special worksheet for each of you. Take a bit of time to ponder these questions and pen down your thoughts. After both of you have completed your worksheets, tuck them away in your time capsule, set to be unveiled on a future date you choose. This is a fun way to capture a snapshot of your relationship now, giving you something special to look back on together.

Create Your Capsule: Place your selected items and letters into a container that can be sealed. As you do this, discuss what each item represents and why it's meaningful to your relationship.

Seal and Date: Seal your time capsule and mark it with a "Do Not Open Until" date. Choose a significant date that's at least one year away, such as an anniversary or a meaningful shared occasion in the future.

Decide on a Safekeeping Spot: Together, choose a special location to store your time capsule, where it will remain undisturbed until the opening date.

Opening Plan: Mark your calendars with the opening date. Agree on how you'd like to celebrate this moment—perhaps with a special meal or a dedicated quiet evening together to reflect on your journey and read your letters aloud.

Outcome:

Through the creation and future opening of this time capsule, couples will not only have a tangible reminder of their love and commitment but also a powerful tool for reflection and connection. This ritual serves as a preventive measure against conflict by reminding both partners of their shared values, hopes, and the enduring strength of their bond. Opening the capsule will offer a unique opportunity to reflect on past challenges and successes, reinforcing the importance of teamwork in overcoming obstacles and nurturing a resilient, loving partnership.

♥ ♥ ♥ ♥ ♥ ♥♥ ♥

Looking ahead, we venture into the next chapter of our journey: "Individual Growth within the Relationship." Here, we'll explore how nurturing your personal development can enrich your partnership, creating a dynamic where both of you flourish, not just as a couple but as individuals. This next step is crucial, for a relationship thrives best when both partners are thriving on their own. So, let's continue forward, carrying the lessons of compassion and understanding into personal growth and mutual support.

WEEK 7 - INDIVIDUAL GROWTH WITHIN THE RELATIONSHIP

A t the heart of every thriving relationship is the ability to dream together and support each other's ambitions. This week, we delve into the foundational aspects of understanding, encouraging, and integrating each partner's dreams and goals within the fabric of a partnership. It's about more than just being in love; it's about being in sync with each other's aspirations, celebrating each victory, and facing setbacks with unwavering support. We explore how identifying and sharing dreams lays the groundwork for a deeply connected relationship, the significance of actively encouraging your partner, the art of setting collaborative goals, and the importance of celebrating each step forward. Through mutual support and shared aspirations, couples can build a relationship that survives and thrives, marked by growth, achievement, and deep, enduring love.

The Importance of Individual Hobbies and Interests

Maintaining Individuality

Your unique qualities and interests play a crucial role in the vitality and resilience of your relationships. Imagine your relationship as a garden. Just like a diverse array of plants makes a garden thrive, your

autonomy and intimacy becomes a source of strength rather than a challenge.

Digital Intimacy: Connecting and Growing Together Online

In today's digitally connected world, our relationships unfold not just in physical spaces but also across digital landscapes. The texts we send, the posts we share, and the digital spaces we inhabit are integral to our relational fabric. As we continue our journey through understanding individual growth within the relationship, we must explore how digital communication influences our connection with our partners, sometimes in ways we might not fully realize.

The Dual-Edged Sword of Digital Connectivity

Digital communication offers the unparalleled advantage of staying connected regardless of physical distance, allowing us to instantly share moments, thoughts, and feelings. Yet, it also presents unique challenges. Without thoughtful engagement, it can create distances, misunderstandings, and feelings of neglect within the very relationships it's supposed to bridge.

Case Study - James and Alex

In the vibrant realm of fashion, where social media threads are intertwined with the very fabric of the industry, James found himself navigating a delicate balance. As a fashion designer, his work demanded an active online presence, engaging with various individuals, including various influential and attractive figures. Though essential, this aspect of his professional life began to stir unease within his relationship with Alex. Alex, fully understanding the professional nature of James's interactions, nonetheless felt discomfort upon seeing these online posts. It wasn't a question of trust but rather the emotional impact of witnessing these interactions unfold in the public domain.

Recognizing the importance of addressing this nuanced challenge, James and Alex embarked on a journey of open communication and empathy. They dedicated time to understanding each other's feelings, with James explaining the professional context of his social media engagements and Alex voicing her emotions and seeking reassurance. Together, they crafted a strategy that allowed James to fulfill his professional obligations while safeguarding their relationship's sanctity. This strategy included setting clear boundaries around social media use, initiating regular check-ins to discuss concerns, and carving out quality time to strengthen their bond away from the digital glare. Their story underscores a vital lesson: even in the face of professional demands, a relationship's strength is measured by the couple's ability to communicate, understand, and support each other, turning challenges into opportunities for growth and deeper connection.

Exercise 1: Digital Detox Date Nights

Once a week, commit to a digital detox date night. From 6 PM onwards, agree to put away all digital devices. Use this time to engage in activities encouraging direct interaction, whether cooking a meal together, playing a board game, or simply talking about your day. This practice isn't about demonizing technology but about creating intentional spaces where your relationship is the sole focus.

Communicating Emotionally in a Digital World

Digital communication strips away many nuances of human interaction. The warmth of a smile, the comfort of a touch, and the reassurance of a tone of voice are often lost in translation. Learning to convey emotions and read emotional nuances in digital communication is a skill that requires attention and practice.

🖤 🖤 🖤 🖤 🖤 🖤🖤 🖤

Exercise 2: Emotional Check-ins

Once a day, initiate an emotional check-in with your partner digitally. Use a text or email to express how you're feeling and ask how your partner is doing. Be intentional with your words—use expressive language to convey warmth and empathy. This practice helps foster emotional intimacy and understanding, even when apart.

🖤 🖤 🖤 🖤 🖤 🖤🖤 🖤

Respecting Digital Independence

In a relationship where the heart often meets the digital age, digital independence is a cornerstone of modern intimacy. It acknowledges each partner's right to engage with digital worlds on their own terms— be it through social media, online gaming, forums, or other digital pursuits. Respecting this digital independence is not just about trust; it's about embracing the complexities of identity and connection in the 21st century. It signifies a mature understanding that personal space— both physical and digital is necessary and healthy even in the closest of bonds.

Understanding Digital Independence

Digital independence in a relationship means recognizing that each partner has digital lives and interests that may not always intersect. It's about valuing privacy and autonomy online, just as we do offline. This respect for digital independence can actually strengthen the bond between partners, fostering trust and a deeper appreciation for each other's individuality.

Fostering Trust in Digital Spaces

Trust is the bedrock of any relationship, and in digital realms, it becomes both a challenge and an opportunity. Respecting your partner's digital independence is a profound expression of trust. It's an understanding that being in a relationship doesn't equate to owning or overseeing every aspect of each other's lives. Trusting your partner online means believing in their discretion and respecting their choices, even when you're not privy to every detail.

Establishing Boundaries

While digital independence is crucial, so is establishing mutual boundaries that protect the integrity of your relationship. These boundaries aren't about restriction but about creating a shared understanding of what is acceptable and what isn't.

♥ ♥ ♥ ♥ ♥ ♥♥ ♥

Exercise 3: Setting Digital Boundaries Together

Sit down with your partner and discuss your online activities, from social media usage to messaging apps and online gaming. Define what each of you considers private and where you're comfortable drawing lines. This could include agreements on sharing personal information, posting about the relationship, or engaging with others online. Remember, these boundaries should be revisited and revised as your relationship evolves. **Celebrating Individuality Online**

Embracing your partner's digital independence is a celebration of their individuality. It acknowledges that each person has interests, hobbies, and communities that enrich them. By supporting your partner's digital pursuits, you're not just respecting their independence but encouraging their growth and happiness.

♥ ♥ ♥ ♥ ♥ ♥♥ ♥

Exercise 4: Digital Heart-to-Heart

Objective: Use specific instances of digital communication discomfort to foster emotional growth, understanding, and a deeper connection between partners.

See Worksheet

Steps:

1. **Select a Recent Example:** Begin by recalling a recent instance where digital communication led to feelings of discomfort for either partner. If you can't remember a specific example, create a hypothetical scenario that could realistically occur, focusing on how it might make one feel uncomfortable.

2. **Prepare for a Heart-to-Heart:** Arrange a dedicated time for a calm, undistracted conversation. This is a chance for both partners to engage in open and supportive dialogue.

3. **Discuss the Example:** Share the example or scenario chosen, detailing what occurred and how it led to feelings of discomfort. This step is crucial for understanding the emotional impact of digital interactions. The focus should be on expressing emotions and seeking understanding, not assigning blame.

4. **Explore Emotions and Needs:** Delve into why this instance was impactful, discussing the underlying emotions and needs. This exploration helps both partners understand each other's perspectives and emotional triggers.

5. **Strategize Together:** Collaboratively develop strategies to address these feelings in the future. This might include setting boundaries around digital communication, finding ways to express needs clearly, or offering reassurance in specific situations.

6. **Affirm Digital Independence and Trust:** Emphasize the importance of maintaining autonomy and privacy in the digital sphere. Discuss how to balance individual digital preferences with the relationship's health, fostering trust and respect.

7. **Reflect and Grow:** After your conversation, reflect on what you learned and how you both felt during the process. Jot down any agreements or insights that could guide your digital interactions moving forward.

Outcome: This exercise aims to turn potential digital pitfalls into catalysts for strengthening your relationship. By addressing specific instances of discomfort, you pave the way for more empathetic, understanding, and connected digital communication.

This approach ensures that your relationship is marked by growth, understanding, and mutual support, even in digital interaction. Respecting digital independence is about more than just managing online activities; it's about honoring your partner's right to privacy, autonomy, and individuality in the digital age. By fostering trust, establishing boundaries, and celebrating each other's interests, couples can navigate the digital landscape in ways that strengthen their relationship. Remember, the goal isn't to monitor or limit but to support and uplift each other in all realms of life, including the vast digital one.

Exercise 5: Digital Space Respect

Discuss and outline digital activities or spaces that you each consider personal. This might include social media interactions, gaming with friends, or online forums. Agree on boundaries that respect these spaces, ensuring both partners feel their individuality is honored within the digital domain.

Objective: Discover and respect each other's favorite online spaces, ensuring both partners enjoy their individual digital worlds.

Steps:

1. **Digital Hangouts:** Each partner shares their favorite online activities or spaces. This might include social media pages,

gaming with friends, or participating in specific forums.

2. **Understand the Significance:** Discuss why these digital zones are personal havens and how to respect these spaces within the relationship. It's about understanding and valuing each other's online preferences.

3. **Agree on Boundaries:** Together, outline boundaries that protect these personal digital activities. These guidelines ensure each person feels their digital individuality is acknowledged and respected.

4. **Balance Individuality and Connection:** Reflect on how these boundaries support both personal growth and the strength of the relationship. It's not about limiting shared activities but enhancing individual freedom and mutual respect.

5. **Maintain Open Communication:** Commit to ongoing conversations about digital boundaries, acknowledging that needs and digital landscapes evolve. Adjusting boundaries as necessary keeps the relationship dynamic and respectful.

6. **Reflective Moment:** After establishing these boundaries, take a moment to discuss the process and its impact on the relationship. Consider how these discussions lead to greater understanding and respect for each other's digital independence.

Conclusion: Acknowledging and respecting personal digital spaces is crucial in today's connected world. This exercise helps ensure that both partners feel their digital preferences are valued, fostering a relationship where individual growth and mutual respect go hand in hand.

🖤 🖤 🖤 🖤 🖤 🖤🖤 🖤

Navigating the digital landscape together has shown us that a little bit of space and a lot of respect go a long way in keeping our connections strong and our hearts closer. Think of it as laying down the foundation for a relationship that's not just about liking each other's posts but truly understanding what makes each other tick, even in the vast digital world. Now, with our digital connection dialed in, let's pivot to something even more exciting—chasing dreams and cheering each other on. It's about to get real as we move from ensuring our online interactions are top-notch to being the ultimate support squad for each other's biggest ambitions. Here's to the next chapter, where dreams take the front seat, and our partnership becomes the powerhouse behind making them come true. Ready to dive in?

Encouraging Each Other's Dreams and Goals

Identifying and Sharing Dreams

Dreams and goals give our lives direction and meaning, shaping our path forward. Within a relationship, sharing these aspirations is vital for understanding each other deeper. It's about revealing parts of your inner world—your hopes, ambitions, and the milestones you wish to achieve. This sharing not only fosters a deeper emotional connection but also aligns your journey together, making your partnership even more meaningful. Encouraging your partner to voice their dreams and listening with an open heart and mind sets the stage for mutual support and understanding.

Active Encouragement

Active encouragement goes beyond mere words; it's about actions that support your partner's pursuit of their goals. This could mean offering practical help, like taking on extra chores to free up their time or providing emotional support through the ups and downs. It might involve brainstorming solutions to obstacles or simply being their biggest cheerleader. Encouragement can also come in the form of resources, whether it's books, courses, or connecting them with people who can help. It's about showing in tangible ways that you believe in them and their dreams.

Collaborative Goal Setting

Setting goals together as a couple is a powerful way to strengthen your bond and ensure you're both moving in the same direction. Start by discussing what you each want to achieve individually and as a couple, then look for areas where your aspirations align or complement each other. Use these discussions to set shared goals that excite both of you. This process can involve both long-term dreams and short-term objectives, creating a roadmap for your future together. Working as a team towards these goals can enhance your sense of unity and partnership.

Celebrating Progress

Acknowledging and celebrating progress is crucial in maintaining motivation and reinforcing the supportive foundation of your relationship. It's about recognizing the big and small milestones and steps forward, appreciating the effort and dedication involved. Celebrating can be as simple as a heartfelt compliment, a special dinner, or a thoughtful gift. These moments of recognition not only boost morale but also remind you of the strength of your partnership and the power of working together towards common goals. It's saying, "I see you, I appreciate you, and I'm with you every step of the way."

Case Study - Alex and Jordan

Alex and Jordan, both avid adventurers at heart, found their relationship hitting a rough patch after moving in together. Initially, their shared love for travel and exploration brought them together, but as daily routines took over, they struggled to maintain their individual passions. Alex, an enthusiastic rock climber, and Jordan, a passionate writer, found themselves sacrificing their hobbies to spend more time together, believing it would strengthen their bond. However, this only led to a growing sense of dissatisfaction and loss of identity for both.

Recognizing the need for change, Alex and Jordan decided to openly discuss their dreams and personal goals, realizing the importance of supporting each other's individual pursuits. They started allocating specific times during the week for their hobbies—Alex joined a local climbing club, while Jordan dedicated evenings to writing. This not only revitalized their spirits but also brought a newfound respect and admiration for each other's dedication and achievements. Celebrating each other's progress and milestones, they found their relationship stronger and more enriched than ever, proving that fostering individual growth was key to their collective happiness.

🖤 🖤 🖤 🖤 🖤 🖤🖤 🖤

Exercise 6: Dream Sharing Date Night

Objective: To deepen understanding and support for each other's dreams and aspirations in a relaxed, intimate setting.

See Worksheet

Steps:

- **Plan a Cozy Evening:** Choose a night to focus on each other without interruptions. Set up a comfortable atmosphere by including things you enjoy, like soft music or your favorite snacks.
- **Prepare Your Dream Lists:** Independently, each partner should jot down their dreams and goals, covering both the near future and long-term aspirations.
- **Share and Explore:** Take turns sharing your dreams with your partner. Explain why each dream matters to you and how you envision achieving it. While listening, show genuine curiosity and encouragement, aiming to fully understand your partner's vision.
- **Engage and Connect:** After sharing each dream, the listener should ask questions to gain a deeper insight. This step is crucial for showing support and interest in your partner's aspirations without immediately jumping to solutions or advice.

Outcome: This exercise strengthens emotional intimacy and mutual understanding. It sets a foundation for ongoing support and encouragement as you both work toward your individual and shared dreams.

As we wrap up Week 7, we've journeyed through the essential dynamics of balancing autonomy with intimacy, embraced the complexities of digital intimacy, and celebrated the power of supporting each other's dreams and goals, each thread weaving into the rich fabric of individual growth within a relationship. These lessons underscore the importance of mutual respect, understanding, and encouraging personal aspirations as cornerstones of a thriving partnership. We've learned that true intimacy involves not just walking side by side but also uplifting each other to reach our highest potential. By integrating these insights, we're reminded that our relationship enriches when we honor our individual journeys, creating a deeper, more supportive bond that fosters both collective and personal fulfillment as we move forward together.

WEEK 8 - GROWING AND FUTURE PLANNING TOGETHER

A s we embark on the final week of our 8-week journey together, it's time to look towards the horizon. This week, "Growing and Future Planning Together," is dedicated to cultivating resilience and adaptability in your relationship. With all its uncertainties and promises, the future requires a solid foundation built on mutual support, understanding, and love. This chapter will guide you and your partner through strategies for facing life's inevitable changes and transitions together. By fostering a dynamic partnership, you're preparing to withstand future challenges and setting the stage for growth, fulfillment, and deeper connection.

Navigating Life Transitions Together

Life is a journey marked by periods of change and growth. As a couple, you will face numerous transitions that will test the strength and adaptability of your relationship. These transitions include career changes, moving to a new city, or starting a family. How you navigate these changes together will significantly impact the health and happiness of your relationship.

Identifying Common Life Transitions

First, let's acknowledge the common transitions you may encounter:

- **Career Changes:** Whether it's a new job, loss of employment, or a shift in career paths, these changes affect time, energy, and sometimes the dynamics of your relationship.
- **Moving:** Relocating involves a physical change of environment and adjusting to new social circles and routines.
- **Starting a Family:** Adding a child brings joy and challenges, requiring adjustments in roles and responsibilities.
- **Health Challenges:** Illness or disabilities can alter the landscape of your relationship, necessitating a new level of care and understanding.
- **Retirement:** This transition can redefine identities, daily routines, and the balance of time spent together.

Strategies for Navigating Transitions

Facing these transitions head-on as a united front involves several vital strategies:

- **Support Each Other:** Provide a supportive ear and a helping hand. Recognize that transitions, even positive ones, can be stressful.
- **Maintain Your Connection:** Keep your relationship a priority. Schedule regular check-ins and quality time together, irrespective of the chaos around.
- **Flexibility:** Be open to modifying your roles within the relationship to better suit your new circumstances.
- **Seek External Support:** External guidance from a therapist or counselor can sometimes provide valuable perspective and coping strategies

Communication During Changes

Open and honest communication is your most powerful tool during times of change. Discuss your fears, hopes, and needs openly. Listen to your partner with empathy and without judgment. Use "I" statements we practiced in our third week to express your feelings and avoid placing blame.

Adapting to New Roles

Transitions often require a shift in roles and responsibilities within the relationship. Approach these changes with an open mind and a willingness to experiment. Discuss expectations and be ready to negotiate and compromise. Remember, the goal is not to return to how things were but to find a new equilibrium that supports both partners.

By embracing change together, you strengthen your bond and ensure that your relationship survives and thrives in the face of life's transitions.

Adapting to Change

As you face the winds of change, your ability to adapt and grow defines the strength and resilience of your bond. This section offers practical exercises designed to enhance your adaptability to change, ensuring you and your partner feel supported and connected, no matter what life throws your way. Let's explore exercises that will help you craft a robust strategy for embracing change together.

Exercise 1: Change Adaptation Plan

Objective: To develop a proactive plan for adapting to anticipated changes while maintaining the strength of your relationship.

See Worksheet

Steps:

1. Together, identify a change you anticipate facing in the near future.
2. Discuss and write down how this change could impact each of you individually and your relationship as a whole. Feel free to leverage a printable worksheet for this exercise included with this workbook.
3. Outline steps you can take to maintain your connection through this transition. Consider weekly check-ins, dedicated quality time, or establishing new rituals.
4. Plan for potential challenges and how you will address them. Agree on specific, actionable strategies.
5. Reflect on a significant change or transition your relationship has previously faced.
6. Discuss how you both felt during this time and your strategies to cope with the change.
7. Identify what you did well as a couple and areas where you could have improved.
8. Use these insights to update your Change Adaptation Plan, ensuring it incorporates your strengths and addresses areas for growth. Feel free to print a new copy of the Change Adaptation Plan worksheet for your periodic check-ins, or even design a custom version that suits your needs better. There's no strict format required. The key to its effectiveness lies in its collaborative creation and mutual agreement between you and your partner.

Outcome: By engaging in these exercises, you'll build a foundation for surviving change and thriving through it together. These practices will enable you to face the future confidently, knowing that your relationship can adapt and grow stronger, no matter what lies ahead.

🐑 🐑 🐑 🐑 🐑 🐑🐑 🐑

Exercise 2: Role-Playing Future Scenarios

Objective: To anticipate potential challenges in upcoming transitions and practice navigating them together. This role-play allows you to explore both your reactions and understand the challenges from the perspective of an external influence affecting your partnership. Through this exercise, you'll practice expressing your feelings and brainstorming solutions as a couple, enhancing your empathy and collaborative problem-solving skills.

Steps:

Select a future scenario or transition you both find daunting.

Take turns role-playing yourselves and potential external influences (e.g., a demanding new job, family pressures). In a situation where you are considering a move, one of you might be role-playing your mother-in-law's response as an example of an external influencer. Please remember that external influencer for this exercise refers to people outside of your couple unit.

Work through the scenario, focusing on communication, support, and problem-solving strategies.

Reflect on the exercise, discussing what you learned about each other's fears and expectations and how you can effectively support one another through similar real-life situations.

🐑 🐑 🐑 🐑 🐑 🐑🐑 🐑

Exercise 3: The Change Resilience Toolbox

Objective: To compile a comprehensive list of resources and strategies that bolster your resilience to change.

See Worksheet

Steps:

1. Together, research and list resources, such as books, podcasts, workshops, and support groups, that could help you adapt to change.
2. Identify strategies that have helped you manage stress and change in the past, like mindfulness, exercise, or journaling.
3. Create a "toolbox" document or a physical box containing these resources and strategies. Ensure it's easily accessible and add to it as you discover new aids.
4. Commit to trying at least one new strategy or resource from your toolbox each month to build your resilience muscles.

Outcome: Upon completing this exercise, you'll have a tailored collection of resources and strategies to bolster resilience against change, symbolizing your joint commitment to support and adapt together. This proactive approach ensures your relationship is equipped to thrive through transitions, enhancing your bond and adaptability as a team.

❦ ❦ ❦ ❦ ❦ ❦❦ ❦

Maintaining Connection Through Change

As you navigate the ebb and flow of life's transitions, your mutual commitment to prioritizing your connection is the rope that anchors your relationship. Changes, whether anticipated or unexpected, test the resilience of your bond. This section focuses on strategies that help sustain and deepen your relationship amidst the whirlwind of life's inevitable shifts.

Prioritizing the Relationship

Core Principle: Your relationship's health and vitality significantly influence how effectively you can manage life's changes together. It's essential to consciously place your relationship at the top of your priorities, even when external demands clamor for your attention.

Strategies:

- Regularly check in with each other about your relationship's health.
- Make time for each other, no matter how busy life gets, ensuring that this time is quality and undisturbed.
- Recognize and celebrate your relationship milestones and the challenges you've overcome together.

Rituals of Connection

Core Principle: Rituals serve as the heartbeat of a relationship, providing a constant rhythm of connection regardless of the changing external circumstances.

Strategies:

- Establish daily rituals that bring you closer, such as sharing a cup of coffee in the morning or reflecting on the day's highlights each night.
- Weekly or monthly rituals, such as date nights or relationship check-ins, can offer deeper moments of connection and reflection.
- Create rituals for navigating change itself, such as a special way of discussing upcoming transitions or a celebratory ritual for overcoming challenges.

Embracing Flexibility

Core Principle: Flexibility in your expectations and plans is crucial as you change together. It allows you to adapt more readily to unexpected circumstances and find joy in the new paths that unfold.

Strategies:

• Practice openness to altering your plans and expectations as situations evolve.

• Cultivate a mindset that views change as an opportunity for growth rather than a setback.

• Discuss and reassess your goals and dreams regularly, acknowledging that they may shift as you grow and change.

Support Systems

Core Principle: While your relationship is a primary source of support, having a broader network of friends, family, and community resources can provide additional layers of stability and perspective during times of change.

Strategies:

• Identify individuals and groups who can offer support, advice, or just a listening ear when you face challenges.

• Engage in community activities or support groups where you can share experiences and strategies with other couples.

• Remember to support others as well; offering support can strengthen your relationships and provide valuable insights.

In embracing these principles, you'll find that your journey through change not only tests but ultimately strengthens your bond. By prioritizing your relationship, maintaining rituals of connection, being flexible, and leaning on your support system, you're equipped to face whatever comes your way with resilience, unity, and a deeper love. Having a support system outside the relationship to lean on during times of change is essential.

Planning for the Future Together

Embarking on creating a shared vision for the future is a powerful way to connect and align with your partner. This section introduces the concept of a vision board for couples, a tangible representation of your collective dreams, goals, and aspirations. Through this creative process, you will visualize your future together and reinforce the strength of your partnership by acknowledging and integrating each other's individual goals.

Shared dreams and goals are the compass that guides your relationship through life's uncertainties. They provide a common direction and a sense of purpose, reinforcing your bond and commitment to each other. This shared vision serves as a reminder of what you're working towards, both as individuals and as a partnership.

Exercise 4: Collaborative Vision Board

Objective: To visually merge both partners' dreams and goals into a collective vision for the future, encompassing all aspects of life you wish to explore and develop together.

Steps:

- **Reflect on Shared Dreams:** Starting with the dreams and goals you shared last week, identify which ones you have in common or are mutually supportive of. Discuss how you can integrate these dreams into a shared vision for your future together.
- **Collect Materials:** Start with a large poster board or digital platform and collect magazines, photos, quotes, and any other items that inspire you.
- **Create Your Vision Board:** Work together to cut out images and phrases that reflect both your individual dreams and your collective goals. Arrange these on a poster board in a way that feels meaningful to you both. The act of creating together should be as enjoyable and meaningful as the outcome itself.
- **Place and Reflect:** Once complete, place the vision board somewhere you can both see it regularly. Use it as a daily reminder of your shared future and as motivation to take steps toward achieving these dreams together.

Outcome: By visually combining your dreams and goals, this exercise solidifies a shared path forward, enhancing your connection and commitment to each other. It serves as a powerful reminder of your shared aspirations, encouraging collaboration and mutual support as you work towards turning these dreams into reality.

💕 💕 💕 💕 💕 💕💕 💕

Incorporating Individual Goals

As you may recall from last week, while shared dreams are vital, individual goals are equally necessary for personal growth and fulfillment. Recognizing and supporting each other's personal ambitions within your relationship demonstrates respect and understanding for one another's unique desires and contributions. This balance ensures both partners feel valued and heard, fostering a healthy, supportive relationship environment.

Updating the Vision Board

As you grow and evolve, so too will your aspirations. Regularly revisiting and updating your vision board is crucial to reflect these changes. Set a yearly or bi-annual "vision board date" to discuss progress, celebrate achievements, and adjust your goals as needed. This ongoing dialogue ensures your shared vision remains relevant and inspiring, adapting to the dynamic nature of your relationship and individual journeys.

Creating a vision board for couples is a transformative exercise that brings you closer and aligns your paths toward a shared future filled with purpose, joy, and mutual fulfillment. It's a vivid reminder of the dreams you're pursuing together and a testament to the strength and adaptability of your partnership.

Keep it Up:

As we conclude our final week together, it is my sincerest hope that this workbook has nurtured growth within your relationship. Embarking on the journey of creating this guide, I recognized the impossibility of offering a one-size-fits-all solution for the myriad complexities of every unique partnership. Therefore, I encourage you to carry forward the insights and strategies you've discovered here. A valuable initial step is to thoughtfully reflect on and pinpoint areas of your relationship you wish to strengthen, setting the stage for focused goal-setting. Together, determine the priorities that demand your immediate attention and agree on objectives that will most positively impact your bond.

Setting clear and actionable goals is crucial in a relationship's journey toward ongoing growth and fulfillment. This section is dedicated to helping you identify the remaining critical areas for development within your relationship, set SMART goals around these areas, and then break these goals down into tangible steps. By focusing on communication, intimacy, adventure, and other foundational pillars, couples can create a roadmap for a relationship that survives and thrives.

♥ ♥ ♥ ♥ ♥ ♥♥ ♥

Exercise 5: SMART Goals for Relationships

Objective: Utilize the SMART framework to create clear, achievable, and tailored goals to further enhance your relationship. Break down each relationship goal into smaller, manageable tasks, creating a clear path toward achievement.

See Worksheet

Guidelines:

- **Specific:** Clearly define what you want to achieve, avoiding vague aspirations. Instead of "spend more time together," opt for "dedicate two evenings each week to quality time."
- **Measurable:** Establish criteria for measuring progress and success. For example, "improve our communication" becomes

"resolve conflicts with a calm discussion at least 80% of the time."
- **Achievable:** Considering your current circumstances, ensure your goals are realistic and attainable.
- **Relevant:** Choose goals that genuinely matter to both of you and will have a positive impact on your relationship.
- **Time-bound:** Set deadlines to keep yourselves accountable. For instance, "plan a weekend getaway within the next three months."

Steps:

1. **Set Goals:** Use the worksheets included to help you identify your relationship goals using SMART framework.
2. **Divide and Conquer:** For each goal, list the specific actions or steps needed to achieve it. Decide who will lead certain tasks or how you will tackle them together. Establish timelines for each task, ensuring they are realistic and provide momentum toward the larger goal.
3. **Track Progress:** Establish a tracking system for monitoring your progress toward relationship goals, allowing for timely modifications as needed. Integrate regular progress discussions into your existing check-in meetings, creating a space to explore your advancements, tackle challenges, and share reflections on the goals you're pursuing together, at intervals that suit you both.
4. **Celebrate Milestones:** Recognize and celebrate when you reach significant points or complete tasks related to your goals.
5. **Adjust as Needed:** Be open to reevaluating and adjusting your goals and strategies. What matters is that the goals continue to serve your relationship and reflect your evolving needs and aspirations.

Setting relationship goals is not just about achieving specific outcomes; it's about embarking on a journey of mutual growth, discovery, and deepening love. By thoughtfully identifying areas for growth, setting SMART goals, breaking them into actionable steps, and monitoring progress, couples can forge a stronger bond and build a fulfilling future together.r monitoring progress towards these goals and adjusting as needed.

❦ ❦ ❦ ❦ ❦ ❦❦ ❦

Achieving goals as a couple is a dynamic and ongoing process filled with successes, challenges, and invaluable learning opportunities. By embracing collaborative goal setting, developing strategies for overcoming obstacles, celebrating milestones, and learning from setbacks, you pave the way for achieving your shared dreams and building a deeper, more resilient partnership.

As we conclude our last week together, we reflect on the journey we've embarked upon, a journey marked by shared visions, set goals, and a deeper understanding of what it means to grow and plan for the future as a couple. This chapter has equipped you with the tools and strategies for crafting a future together and emphasized the importance of teamwork, resilience, and celebration along the way. The exercises and discussions presented are designed to fortify your bond, ensuring that as you move forward, you do so with a strengthened connection, ready to embrace the joys and challenges that lie ahead. Remember, the future you envision and work towards is not just a destination but a testament to your journey of love, growth, and mutual support. Let this chapter serve as a foundation upon which you build a future filled with shared dreams, achievements, and endless possibilities, nurturing a relationship that survives and thrives in the face of change.

CASE STUDY: YOU

As we conclude our journey together, you may have noticed the absence of a traditional case study in the final week's chapter. Instead, I invite you to step into the spotlight. Reflect on the moment you made the conscious decision to enhance your relationship by engaging with this workbook. Consider the effort you and your partner have invested, and acknowledge your progress together. Your story is the most vital case study of all, and I'm eager to learn about your journey. I encourage you to share your experiences and the insights you've gained from this workbook. Your feedback is invaluable, not only to me but also to others on similar paths.

Please take a moment to leave a review on Amazon and share how this book has impacted your connection.
If you reside outside of US, please use the link in your order.

All it takes is 60 seconds to make a difference!

CONCLUSION

As we conclude our eight-week journey, it's time to honor the transformative path you have traveled. This workbook, anchored in the principles of EFT, was not just a set of exercises but a crucible for growth, offering you strategies and insights to fortify your partnership.

Consider how you've intertwined your experiences and lessons into a strong, resilient bond—much like the rope on this workbook's cover. This rope is symbolic of your journey, each strand an essential part of the whole, each twist a challenge you've faced and overcome together. Every week, you've added another strand to this rope, enhancing its strength and your capacity to hold fast to one another when the winds of life blow fiercely.

You've charted a course through communication, trust, and the delicate balance of individuality within togetherness. You've harnessed the digital landscape to preserve your bond and championed each other's ambitions, recognizing that these endeavors aren't isolated paths but essential elements of the shared journey that shapes your life together.

As you look to the horizon, know that the skills you've honed here are designed to support and secure. They are your constant companions through the ebb and flow of life's transitions. Adaptability, the very essence of survival and growth, is now woven into the fabric of your relationship. Keep these lessons close, like a trusted compass, as you build and navigate your future together.

As a life coach, my greatest aspiration is to see you emerge stronger, with a profound sense of clarity and purpose in your partnership. As you turn this book's cover closed, let the rope image be a lasting emblem of your commitment to cultivating a deep and enduring connection.

My heartfelt thanks go to both of you for embracing this journey with openness and dedication. May the bond you've fortified here carry you forward in the easy stretches and through every twist and turn. Your shared narrative is still being written, and the strength you draw from one another will help you climb to new heights and secure the legacy of your love for years to come.

ALSO BY TAYLOR BLAKE

How To Stop Being Toxic and Build Healthy Relationships

REFERENCES

Aron, A., Melinat, E., Aron, E. N., Vallone, R. D., & Bator, R. J. (1997). The experimental generation of interpersonal closeness: A procedure and some preliminary findings. Personality and Social Psychology Bulletin, 23(4), 363-377. Retrieved from Greater Good in Action: https://ggia.berkeley.edu/practice/ 36_questions_for_increasing_closeness

Brennan, K.A., Clark, C.L., & Shaver, P.R. (1998). "Experiences in Close Relationships-Revised (ECR-R) Questionnaire.

https://counselingwellnesspgh.com/top-5-rituals-to-create-connection-in-your-relationship/

https://coupleslearn.com/rebuild-trust-after-betrayal/

https://eugenetherapy.com/article/building-resilience-through-relationships/

https://greatergood.berkeley.edu/article/item/john_gottman_on_trust_and_betrayal

Gottman, J., & Silver, N. (2015). The Seven Principles for Making Marriage Work: A Practical Guide from the Country's Foremost Relationship Expert. Harmony.

https://heightsfamilycounseling.com/blog/2020/10/24/how-self-esteem-affects-your-communication-style

https://holdinghopemft.com/active-listening-a-key-to-deeper-intimacy-and-understanding-in-your-relationship/

How to Help Someone with Anxiety - Jamworks AI Note Taking App. https://jamworks. com/news/how-to-help-someone-with-anxiety/

https://horizoncounselingservicesut.com/30-must-try-couples-therapy-exercises-and-activities/

https://iamreddi.com/post/navigating-relationships-understanding-attachment-style-pairings

Johnson, S. M. (2008). Hold Me Tight: Seven Conversations for a Lifetime of Love. Little, Brown Spark.

Johnson, S. M., & Greenberg, L. S. (Eds.). (1994). The Heart of the Matter: Perspectives on Emotion in Marital Therapy. Brunner/Mazel.

https://journals.sagepub.com/doi/pdf/10.1177/0146167297234003

https://lukincenter.com/the-nine-steps-of-emotionally-focused-therapy-for-couples/

https://marriage.com/advice/communication/barriers-to-effective-communication-in-marriage/

https://marriage.com/advice/relationship/smart-goals-examples-to-improve-your-relationship/

https://marriage.com/advice/relationship/vision-board-for-couples/

https://ncbi.nlm.nih.gov/pmc/articles/PMC4845754/

https://ncbi.nlm.nih.gov/pmc/articles/PMC7058563/

https://ncbi.nlm.nih.gov/pmc/articles/PMC8932676/

https://npr.org/2022/02/09/1079587715/whats-your-attachment-style-quiz

Perel, E. (2017). The State of Affairs: Rethinking Infidelity. Harper.

References

https://plantationcounseling.com/post/the-importance-of-rituals-and-traditions-in-relationships/

https://positivepsychology.com/assertiveness-training/

https://positivepsychology.com/conflict-resolution-relationships/

https://positivepsychology.com/emotion-focused-couples-therapy/

https://positivepsychology.com/emotionally-focused-therapy/

https://psychalive.org/embracing-vulnerability-strengthens-connections/

https://psychalive.org/preserving-individuality-strengthen-relationship/

https://psychologytoday.com/us/blog/mindful-relationships/202101/the-most-effective-couples-therapy-by-
far

https://psychologytoday.com/us/blog/sexual-mindfulness/202207/why-non-sexual-touch-is-so-essential

https://randigunther.com/post/the-role-of-individual-growth-in-successful-couples-counseling

https://riveroakspsychology.com/12-proven-trust-building-exercises-to-repair-relationships-of-all-types/

Schnarch, D. (2009). Intimacy & Desire: Awaken the Passion in Your Relationship. Beaufort Books.

https://talkspace.com/blog/communication-exercises-for-couples-therapy/

https://talkspace.com/blog/relationship-problems/

https://the-conflictexpert.com/2019/04/08/how-empathy-can-resolve-and-prevent-conflict/

https://theknot.com/content/date-ideas

https://thetherapyroomflorida.com/a-guide-to-emotionally-focused-therapy-for-individuals/

https://thebyuido.org/2019/10/the-relationship-needs-circle-way-to.html

https://verywellmind.com/assertiveness-can-improve-your-relationships-7500841

https://verywellmind.com/managing-conflict-in-relationships-communication-tips-3144967

Made in the USA
Middletown, DE
06 October 2024

62097929R00076